Working Papers

for use with

VOLUME ONE

Fundamental Accounting Principles

Thirteenth Canadian Edition

Working Papers

for use with

Fundamental
Accounting Principles

Working Papers
for use with

VOLUME ONE

Fundamental
Accounting Principles

Thirteenth Canadian Edition

Kermit D. Larson
University of Texas—Austin

Tilly Jensen
Athabasca University

Prepared by
Tilly Jensen

McGraw-Hill Ryerson
Connect. Learn. Succeed.

McGraw-Hill
Ryerson
Connect. Learn. Succeed.

Working Papers for use with
Fundamental Accounting Principles
Thirteenth Canadian Edition
Volume 1

ISBN-13: 978-0-07-000035-3
ISBN-10: 0-07-000035-2

1 2 3 4 5 6 7 8 9 10 MP 1 9 8 7 6 5 4 3 2 1 0

Printed and bound in Canada.

Care has been taken to trace ownership of copyright material contained in this text; however, the publisher will welcome any information that enables them to rectify any reference or credit for subsequent editions.

Vice-President and Editor-in-Chief: Joanna Cotton
Executive Sponsoring Editor: Rhondda McNabb
Executive Marketing Manager: Joy Armitage Taylor
Developmental Editor: Melanie Berthier
Supervising Editor: Jessica Barnoski
Team Lead, Production: Jennifer Hall
Cover Design: Dave Murphy
Page Layout: SR Nova Pvt Ltd, Bangalore, India
Printer: Maracle Press

Contents

_____
_____
_____
_____
_____
_____
_____
_____
_____
_____
_____
_____

Quick Study 1-2

a. _____

b. _____

c. _____

d. _____

_____

Quick Study 1-3

a. _____
b. _____
c. _____
d. _____
e. _____
f. _____

Quick Study 1-4

_____
_____
_____
_____
_____
_____
_____
_____

_____
_____
_____
_____
_____
_____
_____
_____
_____
_____
_____
_____
_____
_____
_____
_____
_____
_____

Quick Study 1-6

_____
_____
_____
_____
_____
_____
_____
_____
_____
_____
_____
_____
_____
_____

Exercise 1-1

a. _____
b. _____
c. _____
d. _____
e. _____
f. _____
g. _____

Name _____

	I or E
Bank manager	
Owner	
Toy supplier	

	I or E
Parent	
Canada Revenue Agency	
Cleaner contracted by TLC Daycare	

Exercise 1-3

_____

_____

_____

_____

_____

_____

_____

_____

_____

_____

_____

_____

_____

_____

_____

_____

Exercise 1-4

a. _____

_____

_____

b. _____

_____

_____

c. _____

_____

_____

d. _____

_____

_____

_____

a. _____

_____

_____

_____

_____

_____

_____

_____

_____

_____

_____

_____

_____

_____

b. _____

_____

_____

_____

_____

_____

_____

_____

_____

_____

_____

_____

_____

_____

_____

_____

_____

c. _____

_____

_____

_____

_____

_____

_____

_____

_____

_____

_____

_____

_____

_____

_____

_____

1. _____
2. _____
3. _____
4. _____
5. _____

Exercise 1-7

1. _____
2. _____
3. _____
4. _____
5. _____

Exercise 1-8

1. _____
2. _____
3. _____
4. _____
5. _____
6. _____
7. _____
8. _____

Problem 1-1A

Characteristic	Type of Business Organization		
	Sole Proprietorship	Partnership	Corporation
Limited liability			
Unlimited liability			
Owners are shareholders			
Owners are partners			
Taxed as a separate legal entity			

Problem 1-1B

a. _____
_____
_____

b. _____
_____
_____

1. _____   5. _____

2. _____   6. _____

3. _____   7. _____

4. _____

Quick Study 2-2

a. _____

b. _____

c. _____

Quick Study 2-3

1. _____   4. _____

2. _____   5. _____

3. _____

Quick Study 2-4

	a.	Delco performed work for a client located in China and collected 8,450,000 RMB (Chinese currency), the equivalent of about $1,320,000 Canadian. Delco recorded it as 8,450,000.
	b.	Delco collected $180,000 from a customer on December 20, 2011, for work to be done in February, 2012. The $180,000 was recorded as revenue during 2011. Delco's year end is December 31.
	c.	Delco's December 31, 2011, balance sheet showed total assets of $840,000 and liabilities of $1,120,000. The income statement for the past 6 years has shown a trend of increasing losses.
	d.	Included in Delco's assets was land and building purchased for $310,000 and reported on the balance sheet at $470,000.
	e.	Delco's owner, Tom Del, consistently buys personal supplies and charges them to the company.

Quick Study 2-5

Assets	=	Liabilities	+	Equity
a.				
b.				
c.				

Assets	=	Liabilities	+	Equity
a.				
b.				
c.				

Quick Study 2-7

a.

b.

Allin Servicing
Income Statement
For Month Ended April 30, 2011

Revenues	$300
Expenses	?
Net income (loss)	?

Allin Servicing
Income Statement
For Month Ended May 31, 2011

Revenues	?
Expenses	$ 85
Net income (loss)	?

Allin Servicing
Statement of Changes in Equity
For Month Ended April 30, 2011

Tim Allin, capital, April 1		$ 50
Add: Investments by owner	$ 30	
Net income	?	?
Total		$255
Less: Withdrawals by owner		?
Tim Allin, capital, April 30		?

Allin Servicing
Statement of Changes in Equity
For Month Ended May 31, 2011

Tim Allin, capital, May 1		?
Add: Investments by owner	$ 60	
Net income	?	$110
Total		?
Less: Withdrawals by owner		75
Tim Allin, capital, May 31		?

Allin Servicing
Balance Sheet
April 30, 2011

Assets		Liabilities	
Cash	$ 60	Accounts payable	$ 25
Equipment	?	**Equity**	
		Tim Allin, capital	?
		Total liabilities	
Total assets	$265	and equity	?

Allin Servicing
Balance Sheet
May 31, 2011

Assets		Liabilities	
Cash	$120	Accounts payable	$ 45
Equipment	?	**Equity**	
		Tim Allin, capital	?
		Total liabilities	
Total assets	?	and equity	?

1. _____

2. _____

Quick Study 2-9

_____ a. Income statement   _____ e. Owner's withdrawals account

_____ b. Statement of cash flows   _____ f. Balance sheet

_____ c. Telephone bill   _____ g. Bank statement

_____ d. Invoice from supplier   _____ h. Sales invoice

Quick Study 2-10

Assets	=	Liabilities	+	Equity
a.				
b.				
c.				
d.				
e.				

Quick Study 2-11

_____ 1. Supplies   _____ 8. Utilities expense

_____ 2. Supplies expense   _____ 9. Furniture

_____ 3. Accounts receivable   _____ 10. Fees earned

_____ 4. Accounts payable   _____ 11. Rent revenue

_____ 5. Equipment   _____ 12. Salaries expense

_____ 6. Tim Roadster's withdrawals _____ 13. Tim Roadster's investments

_____ 7. Notes payable   _____ 14. Net income

Quick Study 2-12

_____ 1. Total revenues

_____ 2. Total operating expenses

_____ 3. Net income

_____ 4. Total assets

_____ 5. Total liabilities

_____ 6. Tim Roadster, capital (April 30, 2011)

_____ 7. Total liabilities and equity

_____	1. Net loss.......................................	$ _____
_____	2. Rent expense	22
_____	3. Rent payable	6
_____	4. Accounts receivable....................	14
_____	5. Joan Bennish's investments in May	30
_____	6. Interest revenue	2
_____	7. Joan Bennish, capital, May 1, 2011.......	0
_____	8. Repair supplies	5
_____	9. Notes payable	25
_____	10. Joan Bennish's withdrawals in May	5
_____	11. Truck...	15
_____	12. Consulting fees earned........................	18
_____	13. Joan Bennish, capital, May 31, 2011.....	
_____	14. Cash..	20

Quick Study 2-14

Income Statement

Statement of Changes in Equity

Balance Sheet

Exercise 2-1

(a) _____

_____

_____

_____

(b) _____

_____

_____

_____

(c) _____

_____

_____

_____

_____

_____

(d) _____

_____

_____

_____

_____

_____

_____

_____

	(a)	(b)	(c)	(d)	(e)
Equity, January 1	$ -0-	$ -0-	$ -0-	$ -0-	
Owner's investments during the year..	60,000		31,500	37,500	150,000
Net income (loss) for the year	15,750	40,500	(4,500)		(8,000)
Owner's withdrawals during the year..		(27,000)	(15,000)	(15,750)	(63,000)
Equity, December 31........................	51,000	49,500		42,750	171,000

Exercise 2-3

Income Statement

Exercise 2-4

Statement of Changes in Equity

Analysis component:

_____

_____

_____

_____

Balance Sheet

Analysis component:

_____

_____

_____

_____

_____

Exercise 2-6

Income Statement

Statement of Changes in Equity

Analysis component:

_____
_____
_____
_____

Exercise 2-8

Balance Sheet

Analysis component:

_____
_____
_____
_____
_____

1. _____
2. _____
3. _____
4. _____

Exercise 2-10

(a) Net Income (Loss) = [   ]
     Supporting Calculations: _____

_____
_____
_____
_____
_____
_____

(b) Net Income (Loss) = [   ]
     Supporting Calculations: _____

_____
_____
_____
_____
_____
_____

(c) Net Income (Loss) = [   ]
     Supporting Calculations: _____

_____
_____
_____
_____
_____
_____

(d) Net Income (Loss) = [   ]
     Supporting Calculations: _____

_____
_____
_____
_____
_____
_____

(a) Assets = _____

    Equity = _____

    Supporting Calculations: _____

_____

_____

_____

_____

_____

_____

(b) Liabilities = _____

    Equity = _____

    Supporting Calculations: _____

_____

_____

_____

_____

_____

_____

Exercise 2-12

	ASSETS			=	LIABILITIES	+	EQUITY
	CASH	+	ACCOUNTS RECEIVABLE	+ OFFICE SUPPLIES =	ACCOUNTS PAYABLE	+	NOEL BRIDGES, CAPITAL
(a)							
(b)							
(c)							
(d)							
(e)							
(f)							

	ASSETS				=	LIABILITIES	+	EQUITY
CASH	+ ACCOUNTS RECEIVABLE	+ PARTS SUPPLIES	+ EQUIPMENT	=	ACCOUNTS PAYABLE	+	STACEY CROWE, CAPITAL
(a)							
(b)							
(c)							
(d)							
(e)							
(f)							
(g)							
(h)							
(i)							

Exercise 2-14

a. _____
b. _____
c. _____
d. _____
e. _____
f. _____
g. _____

Exercise 2-15

a. _____
b. _____
c. _____
d. _____
e. _____
f. _____
g. _____
h. _____

	ASSETS			=	LIABILITIES	+	EQUITY	
CASH	+	ACCOUNTS RECEIVABLE	+	EQUIPMENT	=	ACCOUNTS PAYABLE	+	ELLEN MANSON, CAPITAL	EXPLANATION OF EQUITY TRANSACTION
(a)								
(b)								
(c)								
(d)								
(e)								
(f)								
(g)								
(h)								
(i)								
(J)								

Exercise 2-17

a. _____

b. _____

c. _____

d. _____

e. _____

f. _____

Name _____

	ASSETS			=	LIABILITIES	+	EQUITY	
CASH	+ ACCOUNTS RECEIVABLE	+ SUPPLIES	+ EQUIP-MENT	=	ACCOUNTS PAYABLE	+	ANNIE DEWEERD, CAPITAL	EXPLANATION OF EQUITY TRANSACTION
(a) ____	_____	_____	_____		_____		_____	_____
____	_____	_____	_____		_____		_____	_____
(b) ____	_____	_____	_____		_____		_____	_____
____	_____	_____	_____		_____		_____	_____
(c) ____	_____	_____	_____		_____		_____	_____
____	_____	_____	_____		_____		_____	_____
(d) ____	_____	_____	_____		_____		_____	_____
____	_____	_____	_____		_____		_____	_____
(e) ____	_____	_____	_____		_____		_____	_____
____	_____	_____	_____		_____		_____	_____
(f) ____	_____	_____	_____		_____		_____	_____
____	_____	_____	_____		_____		_____	_____
(g) ____	_____	_____	_____		_____		_____	_____
____	_____	_____	_____		_____		_____	_____

Annie Deweerd – Freelance Writing
Income Statement
For Month Ended March 31, 2011

Revenues:
    Freelance service revenue ....
Operating expenses:
    Salaries expense ....
    Rent expense...
        Total operating expenses.................................
Net income...

Annie Deweerd – Freelance Writing
Statement of Changes in Equity
For Month Ended March 31, 2011

Annie Deweerd, capital, March 1 ....
Add: Investment by owner ....
        Net income..
Annie Deweerd, capital, March 31 ....

Annie Deweerd – Freelance Writing
Balance Sheet
March 31, 2011

      Assets

                                Liabilities
Cash ....   Accounts payable ....
Accounts receivable .
Supplies ....
Equipment.................

                                  Equity
                                  Annie Deweerd, capital......................
Total assets ....   Total liabilities and equity.................

Analysis component:

_____
_____
_____
_____
_____
_____
_____
_____

		ASSETS				=	LIABILITIES	+	EQUITY	
CASH	+	ACCOUNTS RECEIVABLE	+	SUPPLIES	+	EQUIP-MENT	=	ACCOUNTS PAYABLE	+	PETE KEQUAHTOO WAY, CAPITAL	EXPLANATION OF EQUITY TRANSACTION
(a)										
(b)										
(c)										
(d)										
(e)										
(f)										
(g)										
(h)										

Exercise 2-21

Income Statement

Statement of Changes in Equity

Balance Sheet

Analysis component:

_____

_____

_____

_____

_____

_____

_____

_____

_____

_____

_____

		ASSETS			=	LIABILITIES	+	EQUITY	
CASH	+	ACCOUNTS RECEIVABLE	+ SUPPLIES +	EQUIP-MENT	=	ACCOUNTS PAYABLE	+	OTTO INGLES, CAPITAL	EXPLANATION OF EQUITY TRANSACTION
Bal.$4,000		$1,200	$900	$7,500		$4,000		$9,600	
(a)									
(b)									
(c)									
(d)									
(e)									
(f)									
(g)									
(h)									

Exercise 2-23

_____

Income Statement

Statement of Changes in Equity

Balance Sheet

Analysis component:

_____
_____
_____
_____
_____
_____
_____
_____
_____
_____

2009 Net Income (Loss) = [   ]
     Supporting Calculations: _____

_____
_____
_____
_____
_____
_____
_____
_____
_____

Problem 2-2A

Income Statement

Statement of Changes in Equity

Balance Sheet

Problem 2-3A

Part 1

Balance Sheet

Balance Sheet

Part 2

Net Income (Loss) Calculation: _____

_____
_____
_____
_____
_____
_____
_____
_____
_____
_____

Analysis component:

_____
_____
_____
_____
_____
_____
_____
_____

Problem 2-4A

Part 1: Company A
(a) _____

_____
_____
_____

(b) _____

_____
_____
_____
_____
_____
_____
_____

(c) _____

_____
_____
_____
_____
_____

Part 2: Company B

(a) _____

_____

_____

_____

(b) _____

_____

_____

_____

_____

_____

(c) _____

_____

_____

_____

_____

_____

_____

_____

Part 3: Company C

_____

_____

_____

_____

_____

_____

_____

_____

_____

_____

_____

_____

_____

_____

_____

_____

_____

_____

Part 4: Company D

_____
_____
_____
_____
_____
_____
_____
_____
_____
_____
_____
_____
_____
_____

Part 5: Company E

_____
_____
_____
_____
_____
_____
_____
_____
_____
_____
_____
_____
_____
_____
_____
_____

Parts 1 and 2

	ASSETS						=	LIABILITIES		+	EQUITY	
	CASH	+ ACCOUNTS RECEIVABLE	+ OFFICE SUPPLIES	+ OFFICE EQUIPMENT	+ BUILDING		=	ACCOUNTS PAYABLE	+ NOTES PAYABLE	+	GEORGE LITTLECHILD, CAPITAL	EXPLANATION OF EQUITY TRANSACTION
(a)												
(b)												
Bal.												
(c)												
Bal.												
(d)												
Bal.												
(e)												
Bal.												
(f)												
Bal.												
(g)												
Bal.												
(h)												
Bal.												
(i)												
Bal.												
(j)												
Bal.												
(k)												
Bal.												
(l)												
Bal.												

Littlechild Enterprises
Income Statement
For Month Ended March 31, 2011

Revenues :
    Service revenue...
Operating expenses:
    Wages expense ....
    Advertising expense ....   _____
        Total operating expenses...................................
Net loss ....   _____

Littlechild Enterprises
Statement of Changes in Equity
For Month Ended March 31, 2011

George Littlechild, capital, March 1
Add: Investment by owner   _____
    Total
Less: Withdrawal by owner
        Net loss   _____
George Littlechild, capital, March 31   _____

Littlechild Enterprises
Balance Sheet
March 31, 2011

Assets		Liabilities	
Cash		Accounts payable	
Accounts receivable		Notes payable	
Office supplies		Total liabilities	_____
Office equipment			
Building			
		Equity	
		George Littlechild, capital	
Total assets	_____	Total liabilities and equity	_____

Analysis component:

_____
_____
_____
_____
_____
_____
_____
_____

Partso 1 and 2

DATE	ASSETS			= LIABILITIES	+ EQUITY	
	CASH	+ ACCOUNTS RECEIVABLE	+ OFFICE SUPPLIES	= ACCOUNTS PAYABLE	+ BEV NG, CAPITAL	EXPLANATION OF EQUITY TRANSACTION

Income Statement

Statement of Changes in Equity

Balance Sheet

Analysis component:

_____

_____

_____

_____

_____

_____

_____

_____

_____

_____

_____

_____

Part 1

DATE	CASH	+ ACCOUNTS RECEIVABLE	+ OFFICE SUPPLIES	+ OFFICE EQUIPMENT	+ ELECTRICAL EQUIPMENT	= ACCOUNTS PAYABLE	+ LARRY POWER, CAPITAL	EXPLANATION OF EQUITY TRANSACTION

Analysis component:

_____
_____
_____
_____
_____
_____

Problem 2-8A

_____

Income Statement

Statement of Changes in Equity

Balance Sheet

Analysis component:

_____
_____
_____
_____
_____
_____

Problem 2-9A

		BALANCE SHEET			INCOME STATEMENT
	TRANSACTION	TOTAL ASSETS	TOTAL LIABILITIES	EQUITY	NET INCOME
1.	Owner invests cash				
2.	Sell services for cash				
3.	Acquire services on credit				
4.	Pay wages with cash				
5.	Owner withdraws cash				
6.	Borrow cash with note payable				
7.	Sell services on credit				
8.	Buy office equipment for cash				
9.	Collect receivable from (7)				
10.	Buy asset with note payable				

2010 Net Income (Loss) = ☐

    Supporting Calculations: _____

_____

_____

_____

_____

_____

_____

_____

_____

_____

Problem 2-2B

Income Statement

Revenues		140000
Rent Revenue		$66000
Total Revenue		
		206000
Operating Expenses:		
O. Supplies Expense	3600	
Utilities Expense	35600	
Wages Expense	92000	
Ad Expense	9000	
Firework Expense	82000	
Net Income		~ 16200

Statement of Changes in Equity

For year ended December 31 2011		
Capital, Jan 1 2011		$375,200
Investments by owner	$30000	
Net Income	(16200)	
Total		389000
Less. Withdrawals		52000
Capital, Dec 31 2011		337000

Balance Sheet

Assets		Liabilities	
		A. Payable	$18000
A. Receivable	$16000		
Building	124000		
Cash	28000		
Firework Supplies	32000	Capital	337000
Land	112000		
Off. Equipment	24000	19+000	
Off. Supp	3000		
Tools	18000		
	355000		355000

Problem 2-3B   Part 1

Balance Sheet

Balance Sheet

Part 2

Net Income (Loss) Calculation:

_____
_____
_____
_____
_____
_____
_____
_____
_____
_____
_____
_____

Analysis component:

_____
_____
_____
_____
_____

Problem 2-4B

Part 1: Company V

(a) _____
_____
_____
_____

(b) _____
_____
_____
_____

(c) _____
_____
_____
_____
_____
_____
_____
_____
_____

Part 2: Company W

(a) _____

_____

_____

_____

_____

(b) _____

_____

_____

_____

_____

_____

_____

_____

(c) _____

_____

_____

_____

_____

_____

_____

_____

Part 3: Company X

_____

_____

_____

_____

_____

_____

_____

_____

_____

_____

_____

_____

_____

_____

_____

_____

_____

Part 4: Company Y

_____
_____
_____
_____
_____
_____
_____
_____
_____
_____
_____
_____
_____
_____
_____
_____
_____
_____

Part 5: Company Z

_____
_____
_____
_____
_____
_____
_____
_____
_____
_____
_____
_____
_____
_____
_____
_____
_____
_____
_____

Parts 1 and 2

CASH	+ ACCOUNTS RECEIVABLE	+ OFFICE SUPPLIES	+ OFFICE EQUIPMENT	+ BUILDING	= ACCOUNTS PAYABLE	+ NOTES PAYABLE	+ BARB TRENT, CAPITAL	EXPLANATION OF EQUITY TRANSACTION
			ASSETS		= LIABILITIES		+ EQUITY	
(a)								
(b)								
Bal.								
(c)								
Bal.								
(d)								
Bal.								
(e)								
Bal.								
(f)								
Bal.								
(g)								
Bal.								
(h)								
Bal.								
(i)								
Bal.								
(j)								
Bal.								
(k)								
Bal.								
(l)								
Bal.								

Trent Consulting
Income Statement
For Year Ended December 31, 2011

Revenues:
    Consulting services revenue ....
Operating expenses:
    Wages expense ....
    Advertising expense ....
        Total operating expenses..................................
Net income...

Trent Consulting
Statement of Changes in Equity
For Year Ended December 31, 2011

Barb Trent, capital, January 1
Add: Investment by owner
      Net income
  Total
Less: Withdrawals by owner
Barb Trent, capital, December 31

Trent Consulting
Balance Sheet
December 31, 2011

Assets	Liabilities
Cash	Accounts payable
Accounts receivable	Notes payable
Office supplies	Total liabilities
Office equipment	
Building	
	Equity
	Barb Trent, capital
Total assets	Total liabilities and equity

Analysis component:

_____
_____
_____
_____
_____
_____
_____
_____
_____

Parts 1 and 2

DATE	ASSETS			= LIABILITIES	+ EQUITY	
	CASH	+ ACCOUNTS RECEIVABLE	+ CLEANING SUPPLIES	= ACCOUNTS PAYABLE	+ KIN PON, CAPITAL	EXPLANATION OF EQUITY TRANSACTION

Part 3

Income Statement

Statement of Changes in Equity

Balance Sheet

Analysis component:

Part 1

DATE	ASSETS						=	LIABILITIES	+	EQUITY	
	CASH	+ ACCOUNTS RECEIVABLE	+ OFFICE SUPPLIES	+ OFFICE EQUIPMENT	+ EXCAVATING EQUIPMENT		=	ACCOUNTS PAYABLE	+	ROBERT CANTU, CAPITAL	EXPLANATION OF EQUITY TRANSACTION

Analysis component:

_____

_____

_____

_____

_____

_____

_____

Problem 2-8B

Income Statement

Statement of Changes in Equity

_____ **Balance Sheet** _____

Analysis component:

_____
_____
_____
_____
_____
_____
_____
_____

Problem 2-9B

	TRANSACTION	BALANCE SHEET			INCOME STATEMENT
		TOTAL ASSETS	TOTAL LIABILITIES	EQUITY	NET INCOME
1.	Owner invests cash				
2.	Pay wages with cash				
3.	Acquire services on credit				
4.	Buy store equipment for cash				
5.	Borrow cash with note payable				
6.	Sell services for cash				
7.	Sell services on credit				
8.	Pay rent with cash				
9.	Owner withdraws cash				
10.	Collect receivable from (7)				

Fundamental Accounting Principles, 13th Edition

1. _____ Buildings
2. _____ Building Repair Expense
3. _____ Wages Expense
4. _____ Wages Payable
5. _____ Notes Receivable
6. _____ Notes Payable
7. _____ Prepaid Advertising
8. _____ Advertising Expense
9. _____ Advertising Payable
10. _____ Unearned Advertising
11. _____ Advertising Fees Earned
12. _____ Interest Earned
13. _____ Interest Expense
14. _____ Interest Payable
15. _____ Earned Subscription Fees

16. _____ Unearned Subscription Fees
17. _____ Prepaid Subscription Fees
18. _____ Supplies
19. _____ Supplies Expense
20. _____ Rent Revenue
21. _____ Unearned Rent Revenue
22. _____ Prepaid Rent
23. _____ Rent Payable
24. _____ Service Fees Earned
25. _____ Jan Sted, Withdrawals
26. _____ Jan Sted, Capital
27. _____ Salaries Expense
28. _____ Salaries Payable
29. _____ Furniture
30. _____ Equipment

Quick Study 3-2

Accounts Receivable

1,000	650
400	920
920	1,500
3,000	

Service Revenue

	13,000
	2,500
	810
	3,500

Cash

3,900	2,400
17,800	3,900
14,500	21,800
340	

Accounts Payable

250	250
900	1,800
650	1,400
	650

Utilities Expense

610	
520	
390	
275	

Notes Payable

4,000	50,000
8,000	

a. _____ Equipment
b. _____ Land
c. _____ Al Tait, Withdrawals
d. _____ Rent Expense
e. _____ Interest Revenue
f. _____ Prepaid Rent
g. _____ Accounts Receivable
h. _____ Office Supplies

i. _____ Notes Receivable
j. _____ Notes Payable
k. _____ Al Tait, Capital
l. _____ Rent Earned
m. _____ Rent Payable
n. _____ Interest Expense
o. _____ Interest Payable

Quick Study 3-4

a. _____ To increase Notes Payable
b. _____ To decrease Accounts Rec'ble.
c. _____ To increase Owner, Capital
d. _____ To decrease Unearned Fees
e. _____ To decrease Prepaid Insurance
f. _____ To decrease Cash
g. _____ To increase Utilities Expense
h. _____ To increase Fees Earned

i. _____ To increase Store Equip.
j. _____ To increase Owner, With.
k. _____ To decrease Rent Payable
l. _____ To decrease Prepaid Rent
m. _____ To increase Supplies
n. _____ To increase Supplies Exp.
o. _____ To decrease Accts. Payable

Quick Study 3-5

a. _____ Buildings
b. _____ Interest Revenue
c. _____ Bob Norton, Withdrawals
d. _____ Bob Norton, Capital
e. _____ Prepaid Insurance
f. _____ Interest Payable
g. _____ Accounts Receivable
h. _____ Salaries Expense

i. _____ Office Supplies
j. _____ Repair Services Revenue
k. _____ Interest Expense
l. _____ Unearned Revenue
m. _____ Salaries Payable
n. _____ Furniture
o. _____ Interest Receivable

Quick Study 3-6

a. _____ Buildings
b. _____ Interest Revenue
c. _____ Bob Norton, Withdrawals
d. _____ Bob Norton, Capital
e. _____ Prepaid Insurance
f. _____ Interest Payable
g. _____ Accounts Receivable
h. _____ Salaries Expense

i. _____ Office Supplies
j. _____ Repair Services Revenue
k. _____ Interest Expense
l. _____ Unearned Revenue
m. _____ Salaries Payable
n. _____ Furniture
o. _____ Interest Receivable

	Cash	101

	Accounts Receivable	106

	Furniture	161

	Accounts Payable	201

	Del Martin, Capital	301

	Revenue	403

Part 2

Cash

Apr. 30 15,000	

Accounts Receivable

Apr. 30 3,200	

Car

Accounts Payable

	6,000 Apr. 30

Unearned Revenue

	1,800 Apr. 30

Dee Bell, Capital

	8,900 Apr. 30

Revenue

	3,000 Apr. 30

Wages Expense

Apr. 30 1,500	

Part 3

_____

_____

_____

_____

GENERAL JOURNAL

Page ____

Date	Account Titles and Explanation	PR	Debit	Credit

GENERAL JOURNAL

Page ____

Date	Account Titles and Explanation	PR	Debit	Credit

Cash   ACCOUNT NO. ____

DATE	EXPLANATION	PR	DEBIT	CREDIT	BALANCE

Office Supplies   ACCOUNT NO. ____

DATE	EXPLANATION	PR	DEBIT	CREDIT	BALANCE

Equipment   ACCOUNT NO. ____

DATE	EXPLANATION	PR	DEBIT	CREDIT	BALANCE

Accounts Payable   ACCOUNT NO. ____

DATE	EXPLANATION	PR	DEBIT	CREDIT	BALANCE

Stan Adams, Capital   ACCOUNT NO. ____

DATE	EXPLANATION	PR	DEBIT	CREDIT	BALANCE

Landscaping Services Revenue   ACCOUNT NO. ____

DATE	EXPLANATION	PR	DEBIT	CREDIT	BALANCE

Trial Balance		
	Debit	**Credit**

Quick Study 3-13

_____
_____
_____
_____
_____
_____

Quick Study 3-14

_____
_____
_____
_____
_____
_____
_____

Quick Study 3-15

_____
_____
_____
_____
_____
_____
_____
_____

Cash	Accounts Receivable
	Office Supplies
Office Equipment	Accounts Payable
Sandra Moses, Capital	Sandra Moses, Withdrawals
Fees Earned	Rent Expense

Cash			Accounts Receivable		
Bal.	700		Bal.	1,200	

			Prepaid Insurance		
			Bal.	-0-	

Computer Equipment			Accounts Payable		
Bal.	480			60	Bal.

Notes Payable			Neil Poundmaker, Capital		
	-0-	Bal.		800	Bal.

Neil Poundmaker, Withdrawals			Service Revenue		
Bal.	-0-			2,600	Bal.

			Wages Expense		
			Bal.	1,080	

Analysis component:

_____
_____
_____
_____
_____
_____
_____
_____
_____
_____

Cash
| Bal. | 1,800 | |

Accounts Receivable
| Bal. | 4,800 | |

Repair Supplies
| Bal. | 1,400 | |

Equipment
| Bal. | 7,400 | |

Accounts Payable
| | | 500 | Bal. |

Nels Sigurdsen, Capital
| | | 2,350 | Bal. |

Nels Sigurdsen, Withdrawals
| Bal. | 500 | |

Repair Revenue
| | | 14,000 | Bal. |

Rent Expense
| Bal. | 950 | |

Exercise 3-4

Parts 1 and 3

Note: T-accounts may be used or the balance column format; both are provided for in Parts 1 and 3 of this exercise.

Cash   101

Accounts Receivable   106

Equipment   150

Accounts Payable   201

Sue Ware, Capital   301

	Sue Ware, Withdrawals 302			Revenue 401

				Expenses 501

Parts 1 and 3

Note: T-accounts may be used or the balance column format; both are provided for in Parts 1 and 3 of this exercise.

GENERAL LEDGER

Cash   ACCOUNT NO. 101

DATE	EXPLANATION	PR	DEBIT	CREDIT	BALANCE

Accounts Receivable   ACCOUNT NO. 106

DATE	EXPLANATION	PR	DEBIT	CREDIT	BALANCE

Equipment   ACCOUNT NO. 150

DATE	EXPLANATION	PR	DEBIT	CREDIT	BALANCE

Accounts Payable   ACCOUNT NO. 201

DATE	EXPLANATION	PR	DEBIT	CREDIT	BALANCE

Sue Ware, Capital   ACCOUNT NO. 301

DATE	EXPLANATION	PR	DEBIT	CREDIT	BALANCE

Sue Ware, Withdrawals   ACCOUNT NO. 302

DATE	EXPLANATION	PR	DEBIT	CREDIT	BALANCE

Revenue   ACCOUNT NO. 401

DATE	EXPLANATION	PR	DEBIT	CREDIT	BALANCE

Expenses   ACCOUNT NO. 501

DATE	EXPLANATION	PR	DEBIT	CREDIT	BALANCE

Part 2

GENERAL JOURNAL   Page _____

Date	Account Titles and Explanation	PR	Debit	Credit

GENERAL JOURNAL   Page ____

Date	Account Titles and Explanation	PR	Debit	Credit

Part 4

Trial Balance

Part 5

Income Statement

Statement of Changes in Equity

Balance Sheet

Analysis component:

_____

_____

_____

_____

_____

_____

_____

_____

_____

_____

_____

Account Number	Account Name	Account Number	Account Name
_____	Cash	_____	Aaron Paquette, Withdrawals
_____	Accounts Receivable	_____	Consulting Revenues
_____	Office Equipment	_____	Salaries Expense
_____	Accounts Payable	_____	Rent Expense
_____	Unearned Revenue	_____	Utilities Expense
_____	Aaron Paquette, Capital		

GENERAL JOURNAL

Page ____

Date	Account Titles and Explanation	PR	Debit	Credit

Part 2

Cash		Accounts Receivable	
Bal.	11,500	Bal.	6,000

		Office Equipment	
		Bal.	12,500

Accounts Payable			Unearned Revenue	
	3,000	Bal.		500	Bal.

Aaron Paquette, Capital			Aaron Paquette, Withdrawals	
	9,500	Bal.	Bal.	2,000

Consulting Revenues			Salaries Expense	
	37,500	Bal.	Bal.	10,000

520	Rent Expense		530	Utilities Expense	
Bal.	7,500		Bal.	1,000	

Part 3

Trial Balance

Part 4

Balance Sheet

Analysis component:

_____

_____

_____

_____

_____

_____

_____

_____

Exercise 3-7

GENERAL JOURNAL   Page _____

Date	Account Titles and Explanation	PR	Debit	Credit
a.				
b.				
c.				

© 2010 McGraw-Hill Ryerson Limited.

GENERAL JOURNAL   Page ____

Date	Account Titles and Explanation	PR	Debit	Credit
d.				
e.				
f.				
g.				

Exercise 3-8

GENERAL JOURNAL   Page ____

Date	Account Titles and Explanation	PR	Debit	Credit

GENERAL JOURNAL   Page ____

Date	Account Titles and Explanation	PR	Debit	Credit

Exercise 3-9

GENERAL JOURNAL   Page ____

Date	Account Titles and Explanation	PR	Debit	Credit

Transactions not creating revenue and the reasons:

_____
_____
_____
_____
_____
_____
_____
_____
_____
_____
_____
_____
_____
_____

Name _____

GENERAL JOURNAL   Page ____

Date	Account Titles and Explanation	PR	Debit	Credit

Transactions not creating revenue and the reasons:

_____
_____
_____
_____
_____
_____
_____
_____
_____
_____
_____
_____
_____
_____
_____

GENERAL LEDGER

Cash   ACCOUNT NO. 101

DATE	EXPLANATION	PR	DEBIT	CREDIT	BALANCE
2010					
Dec. 31	Beginning balance				850

Accounts Receivable   ACCOUNT NO. 106

DATE	EXPLANATION	PR	DEBIT	CREDIT	BALANCE
2010					
Dec. 31	Beginning balance				300

Equipment   ACCOUNT NO. 167

DATE	EXPLANATION	PR	DEBIT	CREDIT	BALANCE
2010					
Dec. 31	Beginning balance				1,500

Accounts Payable   ACCOUNT NO. 201

DATE	EXPLANATION	PR	DEBIT	CREDIT	BALANCE
2010					
Dec. 31	Beginning balance				325

Jay Walker, Capital   ACCOUNT NO. 301

DATE	EXPLANATION	PR	DEBIT	CREDIT	BALANCE
2010					
Dec. 31	Beginning balance				2,325

Jay Walker, Withdrawals   ACCOUNT NO. 302

DATE	EXPLANATION	PR	DEBIT	CREDIT	BALANCE
2010					
Dec. 31	Beginning balance				300

Fees Earned   ACCOUNT NO. 401

DATE	EXPLANATION	PR	DEBIT	CREDIT	BALANCE
2010					
Dec. 31	Beginning balance				1,800

Salaries Expense   ACCOUNT NO. 622

DATE	EXPLANATION	PR	DEBIT	CREDIT	BALANCE
2010					
Dec. 31	Beginning balance				1,500

Analysis component:

_____

_____

_____

_____

_____

_____

_____

_____

_____

_____

_____

GENERAL JOURNAL

Page _____

Date	Account Titles and Explanation	PR	Debit	Credit

Cash

ACCOUNT NO. 101

DATE	EXPLANATION	PR	DEBIT	CREDIT	BALANCE

Office Supplies

ACCOUNT NO. 124

DATE	EXPLANATION	PR	DEBIT	CREDIT	BALANCE

Prepaid Rent   ACCOUNT NO. 131

DATE	EXPLANATION	PR	DEBIT	CREDIT	BALANCE

Photography Equipment   ACCOUNT NO. 167

DATE	EXPLANATION	PR	DEBIT	CREDIT	BALANCE

Joseph Eetok, Capital   ACCOUNT NO. 301

DATE	EXPLANATION	PR	DEBIT	CREDIT	BALANCE

Photography Fees Earned   ACCOUNT NO. 401

DATE	EXPLANATION	PR	DEBIT	CREDIT	BALANCE

Utilities Expense   ACCOUNT NO. 690

DATE	EXPLANATION	PR	DEBIT	CREDIT	BALANCE

Trial Balance

	Debit	Credit

Analysis component:

_____
_____
_____
_____

Cash	**101**

Office Supplies	**124**

Photography Equipment	**167**

Prepaid Rent	**131**

Photography Fees Earned	**401**

Joseph Eetok, Capital	**301**

Utilities Expense	**690**

Trial Balance

	Debit	Credit

Analysis component:

_____
_____
_____
_____
_____
_____
_____
_____
_____
_____

Income Statement

Statement of Changes in Equity

Balance Sheet

Analysis component:

Income Statement

Statement of Changes in Equity

Balance Sheet

Income Statement

Statement of Changes in Equity

Balance Sheet

	Description	(1) Difference between Debit and Credit Column	(2) Column with the Larger Total	(3) Identify account(s) incorrectly stated	(4) Amount that account(s) is overstated or understated
a.	A $2,400 debit to Rent Expense was posted as a $1,590 debit.	$810	Credit	Rent Expense	Rent Expense is understated by $810
b.	A $42,000 debit to Machinery was posted as a debit to Accounts Payable.				
c.	A $4,950 credit to Services Revenue was posted as a $495 credit.				
d.	A $1,440 debit to Store Supplies was not posted at all.				
e.	A $2,250 debit to Prepaid Insurance was posted as a debit to Insurance Expense.				
f.	A $4,050 credit to Cash was posted twice as two credits to the Cash account.				
g.	A $9,900 debit to the owner's withdrawals account was debited to the owner's capital account.				

Exercise 3-19

a. _____

b. _____

c. _____

d. _____

e. _____

Case A: _____

Case B: _____

Case C: _____

Parts 1 and 2

Cash		Land

	Accounts Payable

	Long-Term Notes Payable

Accounts Receivable		Jeff Bridges, Capital

Office Supplies		Jeff Bridges, Withdrawals

Automobiles		Fees Earned

Office Equipment		Wages Expense

	Utilities Expense

Building	

Name _____

GENERAL JOURNAL

Page ____

Date	Account Titles and Explanation	PR	Debit	Credit

GENERAL JOURNAL   Page ____

Date	Account Titles and Explanation	PR	Debit	Credit

Problem 3-3A

GENERAL JOURNAL   Page ____

Date	Account Titles and Explanation	PR	Debit	Credit

GENERAL JOURNAL

Page ____

Date		Account Titles and Explanation	PR	Debit	Credit
2011					
Mar	1	Cash	101	50,000	
		Office equipment		12,000	
		Claude Flynne, Capital			62,000
		Investment			
Mar	1	Prepaid rent		3600	
		Cash			3600
		Prepaid rent for three months			
Mar	3	Office Equipment		6000	
		Office Supplies		1200	
		Accounts Payable			7200-
		Purchase Office Equip & Supplies on Cr			
Mar	5	Cash		1,000	
		Accounting Fees Earned			1,000
		Received cash from client for completed work			
Mar	9	Accounts Receivable		4,000	
		Accounting Fees Earned			4,000

Problem 3-4A   Parts 1 and 2

GENERAL LEDGER

Cash   ACCOUNT NO. 101

DATE	EXPLANATION	PR	DEBIT	CREDIT	BALANCE

Accounts Receivable   ACCOUNT NO. 106

DATE	EXPLANATION	PR	DEBIT	CREDIT	BALANCE

Office Supplies   ACCOUNT NO. 124

DATE	EXPLANATION	PR	DEBIT	CREDIT	BALANCE

Prepaid Insurance   ACCOUNT NO. 128

DATE	EXPLANATION	PR	DEBIT	CREDIT	BALANCE

Prepaid Rent   ACCOUNT NO. 131

DATE	EXPLANATION	PR	DEBIT	CREDIT	BALANCE

Office Equipment   ACCOUNT NO. 163

DATE	EXPLANATION	PR	DEBIT	CREDIT	BALANCE

Accounts Payable   ACCOUNT NO. 201

DATE	EXPLANATION	PR	DEBIT	CREDIT	BALANCE

Claude Flynne, Capital   ACCOUNT NO. 301

DATE	EXPLANATION	PR	DEBIT	CREDIT	BALANCE

Claude Flynne, Withdrawals   ACCOUNT NO. 302

DATE	EXPLANATION	PR	DEBIT	CREDIT	BALANCE

Accounting Fees Earned   ACCOUNT NO. 401

DATE	EXPLANATION	PR	DEBIT	CREDIT	BALANCE

Utilities Expense   ACCOUNT NO. 690

DATE	EXPLANATION	PR	DEBIT	CREDIT	BALANCE

Part 3

Trial Balance

Parts 1 and 2

| Cash | 101 | | Accounts Payable | 201 |
| | | | | |

| Claude Flynne, Capital | 301 |
| | |

| Claude Flynne, Withdrawals | 302 |
| | |

| Accounts Receivable | 106 |
| | |

| Accounting Fees Earned | 401 |
| | |

| Office Supplies | 124 | | Utilities Expense | 690 |
| | | | | |

| Prepaid Insurance | 128 |
| | |

| Prepaid Rent | 131 |
| | |

| Office Equipment | 163 |
| | |

Part 3: *Prepare the trial balance on the page provided for Part 3 of Problem 3-4A.*

GENERAL JOURNAL   Page ____

Date	Account Titles and Explanation	PR	Debit	Credit

GENERAL JOURNAL

Date	Account Titles and Explanation	PR	Debit	Credit

Parts 2 and 3

GENERAL LEDGER

Cash   ACCOUNT NO. 101

DATE	EXPLANATION	PR	DEBIT	CREDIT	BALANCE

Accounts Receivable — ACCOUNT NO. 106

DATE	EXPLANATION	PR	DEBIT	CREDIT	BALANCE

Office Supplies — ACCOUNT NO. 124

DATE	EXPLANATION	PR	DEBIT	CREDIT	BALANCE

Prepaid Insurance — ACCOUNT NO. 128

DATE	EXPLANATION	PR	DEBIT	CREDIT	BALANCE

Prepaid Rent — ACCOUNT NO. 131

DATE	EXPLANATION	PR	DEBIT	CREDIT	BALANCE

Office Equipment — ACCOUNT NO. 163

DATE	EXPLANATION	PR	DEBIT	CREDIT	BALANCE

Accounts Payable — ACCOUNT NO. 201

DATE	EXPLANATION	PR	DEBIT	CREDIT	BALANCE

Jill Wahpoosywan, Capital — ACCOUNT NO. 301

DATE	EXPLANATION	PR	DEBIT	CREDIT	BALANCE

Jill Wahpoosywan, Withdrawals — ACCOUNT NO. 302

DATE	EXPLANATION	PR	DEBIT	CREDIT	BALANCE

Services Revenue   ACCOUNT NO. 403

DATE	EXPLANATION	PR	DEBIT	CREDIT	BALANCE

Utilities Expense   ACCOUNT NO. 690

DATE	EXPLANATION	PR	DEBIT	CREDIT	BALANCE

Part 4

Trial Balance

Analysis component:

_____
_____
_____
_____
_____
_____
_____
_____
_____
_____
_____

Part 1: *Journalize the entries on the Journal page provided in Part 1 of Problem 3-6A.*
Part 2

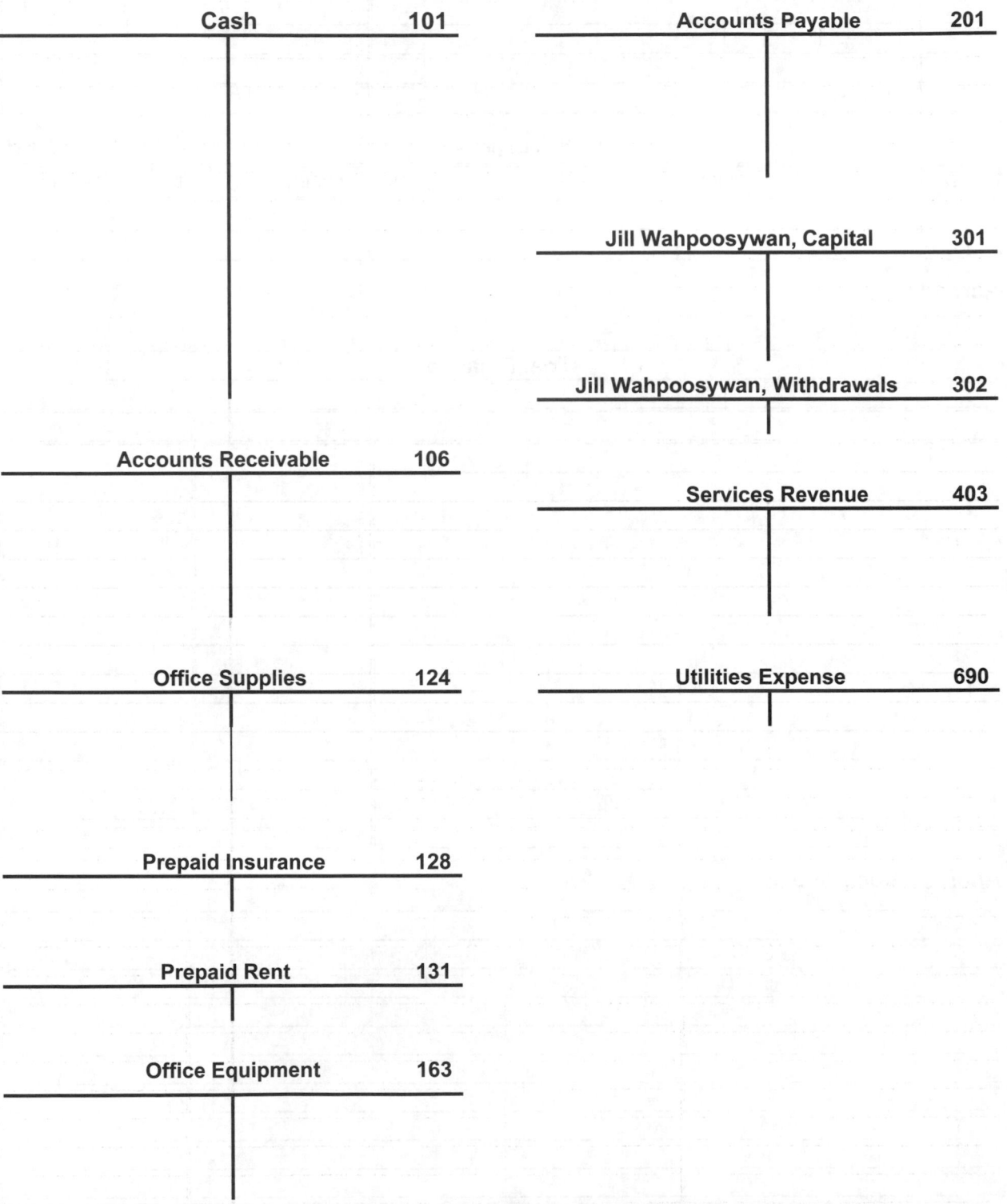

Cash	101

Accounts Payable	201

Jill Wahpoosywan, Capital	301

Jill Wahpoosywan, Withdrawals	302

Accounts Receivable	106

Services Revenue	403

Office Supplies	124

Utilities Expense	690

Prepaid Insurance	128

Prepaid Rent	131

Office Equipment	163

Part 4 and Analysis component: *Prepare on the page provided in Part 4 of Problem 3-6A.*

Income Statement

Statement of Changes in Equity

Balance Sheet

Analysis component: **GENERAL JOURNAL**   Page____

Date		Account Titles and Explanation	PR	Debit	Credit

Problem 3-9A

GENERAL JOURNAL   Page____

Date		Account Titles and Explanation	PR	Debit	Credit

GENERAL JOURNAL　　　　　　　　　Page____

Date	Account Titles and Explanation	PR	Debit	Credit

GENERAL JOURNAL   Page____

Date	Account Titles and Explanation	PR	Debit	Credit

Parts 2 and 3

GENERAL LEDGER

Cash   ACCOUNT NO. 101

DATE	EXPLANATION	PR	DEBIT	CREDIT	BALANCE
2011					
Jun. 30	Beginning balance				26,000

Accounts Receivable   ACCOUNT NO. 106

DATE	EXPLANATION	PR	DEBIT	CREDIT	BALANCE
2011					
Jun. 30	Beginning balance				3,000

Prepaid Insurance   ACCOUNT NO. 128

DATE	EXPLANATION	PR	DEBIT	CREDIT	BALANCE
2011					
Jun. 30	Beginning balance				500

Office Equipment   ACCOUNT NO. 163

DATE	EXPLANATION	PR	DEBIT	CREDIT	BALANCE
2011					
Jun. 30	Beginning balance				1,700

Drafting Equipment   ACCOUNT NO. 167

DATE	EXPLANATION	PR	DEBIT	CREDIT	BALANCE
2011					
Jun. 30	Beginning balance				1,200

Building   ACCOUNT NO. 173

DATE	EXPLANATION	PR	DEBIT	CREDIT	BALANCE
2011					
Jun. 30	Beginning balance				42,000

Land   ACCOUNT NO. 183

DATE	EXPLANATION	PR	DEBIT	CREDIT	BALANCE
2011					
Jun. 30	Beginning balance				28,000

Accounts Payable   ACCOUNT NO. 201

DATE	EXPLANATION	PR	DEBIT	CREDIT	BALANCE
2011					
Jun. 30	Beginning balance				1,740

Long-Term Notes Payable   ACCOUNT NO. 251

DATE	EXPLANATION	PR	DEBIT	CREDIT	BALANCE
2011					
Jun. 30	Beginning balance				24,000

Bishr Binbutti, Capital   ACCOUNT NO. 301

DATE	EXPLANATION	PR	DEBIT	CREDIT	BALANCE
2011					
Jun. 30	Beginning balance				54,000

Bishr Binbutti, Withdrawals   ACCOUNT NO. 302

DATE	EXPLANATION	PR	DEBIT	CREDIT	BALANCE
2011					
Jun. 30	Beginning balance				1,000

Engineering Fees Earned   ACCOUNT NO. 401

DATE	EXPLANATION	PR	DEBIT	CREDIT	BALANCE
2011					
Jun. 30	Beginning balance				29,600

Wages Expense   ACCOUNT NO. 623

DATE	EXPLANATION	PR	DEBIT	CREDIT	BALANCE
2011					
Jun. 30	Beginning balance				4,000

Equipment Rental Expense   ACCOUNT NO. 645

DATE	EXPLANATION	PR	DEBIT	CREDIT	BALANCE
2011					
Jun. 30	Beginning balance				1,000

Advertising Expense   ACCOUNT NO. 655

DATE	EXPLANATION	PR	DEBIT	CREDIT	BALANCE
2011					
Jun. 30	Beginning balance				640

Repairs Expense   ACCOUNT NO. 684

DATE	EXPLANATION	PR	DEBIT	CREDIT	BALANCE
2011					
Jun. 30	Beginning balance				300

Parts 4

Trial Balance

Part 1: *Journalize the entries in the general journal pages provided for Problem 3-9A.*
Parts 2 and 3

Cash	101
Bal. 26,000	

Accounts Receivable	106
Bal. 3,000	

Prepaid Insurance	128
Bal. 500	

Office Equipment	163
Bal. 1,700	

Drafting Equipment	167
Bal. 1,200	

Building	173
Bal. 42,000	

Land	183
Bal. 28,000	

Accounts Payable	201
	1,740 Bal.

Long-Term Notes Payable	251
	24,000 Bal.

Bishr Binbutti, Capital	301
	54,000 Bal.

Bishr Binbutti, Withdrawals	302
Bal. 1,000	

Engineering Fees Earned	401
	29,600 Bal.

Wages Expense	623
Bal. 4,000	

Equipment Rental Expense	645
Bal. 1,000	

Advertising Expense	655
Bal. 640	

Repairs Expense	684
Bal. 300	

Part 4: *Prepare the trial balance on the page provided for Part 4 of Problem 3-9A.*

Problem 3-11A   Part 1

GENERAL JOURNAL   Page____

Date	Account Titles and Explanation	PR	Debit	Credit

GENERAL JOURNAL   Page____

Date	Account Titles and Explanation	PR	Debit	Credit

Parts 2 and 3

	Cash	101
Bal.	6,000	

	Supplies	126
Bal.	950	

	Furniture	161
Bal.	8,000	

Accounts Payable		201
	1,500	Bal.

Unearned Teaching Revenue		233
	9,800	Bal.

Ted Ng, Capital		301
	3,000	Bal.

Ted Ng, Withdrawals		302
Bal.	13,000	

Teaching Revenue		401
	46,000	Bal.

Wages Expense		623
Bal.	26,350	

Rent Expense		640
Bal.	6,000	

Part 4

Trial Balance		

Income Statement

Statement of Changes in Equity

Balance Sheet

Income Statement

Statement of Changes in Equity

Balance Sheet

Analysis component:

GENERAL JOURNAL   Page____

Date	Account Titles and Explanation	PR	Debit	Credit

Problem 3-13A

Trial Balance

Calculations:

_____
_____
_____
_____
_____
_____
_____
_____

Name _____

Parts 1 and 2

Cash		Land

Accounts Payable

Accounts Receivable		Long-Term Notes Payable

	Trevor Peeters, Capital

Office Supplies		Trevor Peeters, Withdrawals

Automobiles		Fees Earned

Office Equipment		Salaries Expense

	Utilities Expense

Building

GENERAL JOURNAL

Date		Account Titles and Explanation	PR	Debit	Credit
Mar	1	Building Expense		375000	
		Cash			75000
		Notes Payable			300000
	1	Prepaid Insurance		5700	
		Cash			5700
	2	Prepaid Hotel		240	
		Accounts payable			240
	4	Supplies		450	
		Accounts Payable			450
	15	Accounts Payable		450	
		Cash			450
	19	Accounts Receivable		35000	
		Service Fees Earned			35000
	20	Cash		8000	
		Accounting fees earned			8000
	28	Accounts Payable		240	
		Cash			240
	29	Cash			
		Service Fees Earned			
	30	Salary Expense		25600	
		Cash			25600
	30	no entry			
	30	Cash		17500	
		Accounts Receivable			17500

GENERAL JOURNAL   Page ____

Date		Account Titles and Explanation	PR	Debit	Credit

Problem 3-3B

GENERAL JOURNAL   Page _1_

Date		Account Titles and Explanation	PR	Debit	Credit
Sep	1	Cash		16,000	
		Office Equipment		4,800	
		Capital			20,800
		Invested cash and equipment			
	1				
	1	Prepaid Rent		4800	
		Cash			4800
		Prepaid 2 months rent			
	2	Office Equipment		4,200	
		Office Supplies		850	
		Accounts Payable			5050
		Purchased eq. and supplies in credit			
	4	Cash		1,900	
		Accounting fees earned			1,900
		Received cash			
	8	Accounts Receivable		3,600	
		Accounts Fees Earned			3,600
		Billed the bank			
	10	Accounts Payable		5050	
		Cash			5050
		Paid balance due on ac. payable			

GENERAL JOURNAL   Page ____

Date		Account Titles and Explanation	PR	Debit	Credit
	14	Prepaid Insurance		3,300	
		Cash			3,300
	15	Prepaid Seminar		1250	
		Cash			1250
	18	Accounts Rec.		3,600	
		Accounts Fees Earned			3600
	20	no entry			
	24	Accounts Receivable		650	
		Accounts Fees Earned			650
	28	Hurley, withdrawals		300	
		Cash			300
		Owners withdrawal of cash			
	29	Office Supplies		450	
		Accounts Payable			450
	30	Utility Bills		730	
		Cash			730

GENERAL LEDGER

Cash — ACCOUNT NO. 101

DATE	EXPLANATION	PR	DEBIT	CREDIT	BALANCE
Mar 1				16,000	16,000
1				480	15520
4			1900		17420
10				5050	12370
14				3300	9070
15				1250	7820
18			3600		11420
28				300	11120
30				730	10390

Accounts Receivable — ACCOUNT NO. 106

DATE	EXPLANATION	PR	DEBIT	CREDIT	BALANCE
Mar. 8			3600		3600
18				3600	0
24			650		650

Office Supplies — ACCOUNT NO. 124

DATE	EXPLANATION	PR	DEBIT	CREDIT	BALANCE
Mar 2			850		850
29			450		1300

Prepaid Insurance — ACCOUNT NO. 128

DATE	EXPLANATION	PR	DEBIT	CREDIT	BALANCE
14			3300		3300

Prepaid Rent — ACCOUNT NO. 131

DATE	EXPLANATION	PR	DEBIT	CREDIT	BALANCE
1			4800		4800

Office Equipment — ACCOUNT NO. 163

DATE	EXPLANATION	PR	DEBIT	CREDIT	BALANCE
1			4800		4800
			4200		9000

Accounts Payable   ACCOUNT NO. 210

DATE	EXPLANATION	PR	DEBIT	CREDIT	BALANCE
2			5050	5050	5050
10			5050		0
29				450	450

Susan Hurley, Capital   ACCOUNT NO. 301

DATE	EXPLANATION	PR	DEBIT	CREDIT	BALANCE
1				20800	20800

Susan Hurley, Withdrawals   ACCOUNT NO. 302

DATE	EXPLANATION	PR	DEBIT	CREDIT	BALANCE
28			300		300

Accounting Fees Earned   ACCOUNT NO. 401

DATE	EXPLANATION	PR	DEBIT	CREDIT	BALANCE
4				1900	1900
8				3600	5500
24				650	6150

Professional Development Expense   ACCOUNT NO. 680

DATE	EXPLANATION	PR	DEBIT	CREDIT	BALANCE

Utilities Expense   ACCOUNT NO. 690

DATE	EXPLANATION	PR	DEBIT	CREDIT	BALANCE
30			730		730

Part 3

September 31, 2011
Trial Balance

Account Title	Debit	Credit
Cash	$ 10390	
A. Receivable	650	
Office Supplies	1300	
	3300	
	4800	
	9000	
		$ 450
		20800
		300
		6150
		730
	29440	28430

Part 1: *Journalize the entries on the journal pages provided in Part 1 of Problem 3-4B.*

Part 2

Cash	101
Sep 1 16000	480 Sep 1
4 1900	5050 10
18 3600	3300 14
	1250 15
	300 28
	7

Accounts Payable	201

Susan Hurley, Capital	301

Susan Hurley, Withdrawals	302

Accounts Receivable	106

Accounting Fees Earned	401

Office Supplies	124

Professional Development Expense 680

Utilities Expense	690

Prepaid Insurance	128

Prepaid Rent	131

Office Equipment	163

Part 3: *Prepare the trial balance on the page provided for Part 3 of Problem 3-4B.*

Credit   Cr   Cr

GENERAL JOURNAL   Page__1__

Date		Account Titles and Explanation	PR	Debit	Credit
Nov	1	Cash		$ 65000	
		Office Eq.		32000	
		Capital			$ 97000
	2	Prepaid Rent		18600	
		Cash			18600
	4	Office. Eq. + Offi Supplies		9000 +1200	
		Accounts Payable			10200
	8	Cash		5200	
		Accounting Fees Earned			5200
	12	Accounts Receivable		6800	
		Accounts Fees Earned			6800
	13	Accounts Payable		10200	
		Cash			10200
	19	Prepaid Insurance		10400	
		Cash			10400
	22	Cash		1800	
		Accounts Receivable			1800
	24	Accounts Receivable		3600	
		Accounting Fees Earned			3600
	28	Amand withdrawal		5300	
		Cash			5300
	29	Office Supplies		1700	
		Accounts Payable			1700
	30	Wages Expense		9000	
		Cash			9000
	30	Utility Expense		1650	
		Cash			1650

GENERAL JOURNAL   Page____

Date	Account Titles and Explanation	PR	Debit	Credit

Parts 2 and 3

GENERAL LEDGER

Cash   ACCOUNT NO. 101

DATE	EXPLANATION	PR	DEBIT	CREDIT	BALANCE
Nov 1			65000		
2				18600	
8			55200		
13				10200	
19				10400	
22			1800		
28				5300	
30				9000	
30				1650	
			16850		

Accounts Receivable   ACCOUNT NO. 106

DATE	EXPLANATION	PR	DEBIT	CREDIT	BALANCE
12			6800		
22				1800	
24			3600		
			8600		

Office Supplies   ACCOUNT NO. 124

DATE	EXPLANATION	PR	DEBIT	CREDIT	BALANCE
4			1200		
29			1700		
			2900		

Prepaid Insurance   ACCOUNT NO. 128

DATE	EXPLANATION	PR	DEBIT	CREDIT	BALANCE
19			10400		
			10400		

Prepaid Rent   ACCOUNT NO. 131

DATE	EXPLANATION	PR	DEBIT	CREDIT	BALANCE
2			18600		
			18600		

Office Equipment   ACCOUNT NO. 163

DATE	EXPLANATION	PR	DEBIT	CREDIT	BALANCE
1			32000		
4			9000		
			41000		

Accounts Payable   ACCOUNT NO. 201

DATE	EXPLANATION	PR	DEBIT	CREDIT	BALANCE
4				10200	
12			10200		
29				1700	
				1700	

Dale Annand, Capital   ACCOUNT NO. 301

DATE	EXPLANATION	PR	DEBIT	CREDIT	BALANCE
1				97000	
				97000	

Dale Annand, Withdrawals   ACCOUNT NO. 302

DATE	EXPLANATION	PR	DEBIT	CREDIT	BALANCE
			5300		
			5300		

Service Fees Earned   ACCOUNT NO. 401

DATE	EXPLANATION	PR	DEBIT	CREDIT	BALANCE
				5200	
				6800	
				3600	
				15600	

Wages Expense   ACCOUNT NO. 680

DATE	EXPLANATION	PR	DEBIT	CREDIT	BALANCE
30			9000		

Utilities Expense   ACCOUNT NO. 690

DATE	EXPLANATION	PR	DEBIT	CREDIT	BALANCE
			1650		

Part 4

Trial Balance

	Debit	Credit
	16850	
	8600	
	2900	
	10400	
	18600	
	61000	
		1700
		97000
	5300	
		15600
	9000	
	1650	
	114300	114300

Analysis component:

Part 1: *Journalize the entries on the Journal page provided in Part 1 of Problem 3-6B.*

Parts 2 and 3

Cash	101

Accounts Payable	201

A ≠ W ↑ Debit
LR.

Dale Annand, Capital	301

Dale Annand, Withdrawals	302

Accounts Receivable	106

Services Fees Earned	401

Office Supplies	124

Wages Expense	680

Prepaid Insurance	128

Utilities Expense	690

Prepaid Rent	131

Office Equipment	163

Part 4 and Analysis component: *Prepare the answers to these on the page provided in Part 4 and the analysis component in Problem 3-6B.*

Income Statement

Statement of Changes in Equity

Balance Sheet

Chapter 3   Problem 3-8B (concl'd.)   *Name* _____

Analysis Component:

GENERAL JOURNAL   Page ____

Date	Account Titles and Explanation	PR	Debit	Credit

Problem 3-9B   Part 1

GENERAL JOURNAL   Page ____

Date	Account Titles and Explanation	PR	Debit	Credit
July 1	Office Equipment		9000	
	Truck		56000	
	Notes Payable			65000
2	Land		124000	
	Cash			40,800
	Notes Payable			83,200
3	Building Expense		21,000	
	Cash			21000
5	Prepaid Insurance		9600	
	Cash			9600
9	Cash		3200	
	Service Fees Earned			3200
12	Office Equipment		6500	
	cash			700
	Notes Payable			5800
15	Accounts Receivable		3750	
	Service Fees Earned			3750

GENERAL JOURNAL

Page ____

Date	Account Titles and Explanation	PR	Debit	Credit
20	Accounts Receivable		9200	
	Service Fees Earned			9200
21	Truck Rental Expense		1300	
	Account Payable			1300
22	Cash		5000	
	Accounts Receivable			5000
23	Wages Expense		1600	
	Cash			1600
24	Accounts Payable		1300	
	Cash			1300
25	Truck Repair Expense		1425	
	Cash			1425
26	Withdrawal		3875	
	Cash			3875
27	Salary expense		1600	
	Cash			1600
28	Advertising Expense		800	
	Cash			800
29	Cash		1400	
	Service Fees Earned			1400

Parts 2 and 3

GENERAL LEDGER

Cash   ACCOUNT NO. 101

DATE	EXPLANATION	PR	DEBIT	CREDIT	BALANCE
2011					
Jun. 30	Beginning balance				75,000

Accounts Receivable   ACCOUNT NO. 106

DATE	EXPLANATION	PR	DEBIT	CREDIT	BALANCE
2011					
Jun. 30	Beginning balance				950

Prepaid Insurance   ACCOUNT NO. 128

DATE	EXPLANATION	PR	DEBIT	CREDIT	BALANCE
2011					
Jun. 30	Beginning balance				275

Trucks   ACCOUNT NO. 153

DATE	EXPLANATION	PR	DEBIT	CREDIT	BALANCE
2011					
Jun. 30	Beginning balance				20,800

Office Equipment   ACCOUNT NO. 163

DATE	EXPLANATION	PR	DEBIT	CREDIT	BALANCE
2011					
Jun. 30	Beginning balance				1,200

Building   ACCOUNT NO. 173

DATE	EXPLANATION	PR	DEBIT	CREDIT	BALANCE
2011					
Jun. 30	Beginning balance				0

Land   ACCOUNT NO. 183

DATE	EXPLANATION	PR	DEBIT	CREDIT	BALANCE
2011					
Jun. 30	Beginning balance				0

Accounts Payable   ACCOUNT NO. 201

DATE	EXPLANATION	PR	DEBIT	CREDIT	BALANCE
2011					
Jun. 30	Beginning balance				725

Unearned Fees   ACCOUNT NO. 233

DATE	EXPLANATION	PR	DEBIT	CREDIT	BALANCE
2011					
Jun. 30	Beginning balance				0

Long-Term Notes Payable   ACCOUNT NO. 251

DATE	EXPLANATION	PR	DEBIT	CREDIT	BALANCE
2011					
Jun. 30	Beginning balance				7,000

Wilf Eazy, Capital   ACCOUNT NO. 301

DATE	EXPLANATION	PR	DEBIT	CREDIT	BALANCE
2011					
Jun. 30	Beginning balance				83,825

Wilf Eazy, Withdrawals   ACCOUNT NO. 302

DATE	EXPLANATION	PR	DEBIT	CREDIT	BALANCE
2011					
Jun. 30	Beginning balance				600

Fees Earned   ACCOUNT NO. 401

DATE	EXPLANATION	PR	DEBIT	CREDIT	BALANCE
2011					
Jun. 30	Beginning balance				8,400

Wages Expense   ACCOUNT NO. 623

DATE	EXPLANATION	PR	DEBIT	CREDIT	BALANCE
2011					
Jun. 30	Beginning balance				780

Truck Rental Expense   ACCOUNT NO. 645

DATE	EXPLANATION	PR	DEBIT	CREDIT	BALANCE
2011					
Jun. 30	Beginning balance				230

Advertising Expense   ACCOUNT NO. 655

DATE	EXPLANATION	PR	DEBIT	CREDIT	BALANCE
2011					
Jun. 30	Beginning balance				75

Repairs Expense   ACCOUNT NO. 684

DATE	EXPLANATION	PR	DEBIT	CREDIT	BALANCE
2011					
Jun. 30	Beginning balance				40

Part 4

Trial Balance

Part 1: *Journalize the entries in the journal pages provided in Part 1 of Problem 3-9B.*
Parts 2 and 3

Cash		101
Bal.	75,000	

Office Equipment		163
Bal.	1,200	

Building		173
Bal.	-0-	

Land		183
Bal.	-0-	

Accounts Receivable		106
Bal.	950	

Prepaid Insurance		128
Bal.	275	

Trucks		153
Bal.	20,800	

Accounts Payable		201
	725	Bal.

Unearned Fees		233
	-0-	Bal.

Long-Term Notes Payable		251
	7,000	Bal.

Wilf Eazy, Capital	301
	83,825	Bal.

Wages Expense	623
Bal.	780	

Wilf Eazy, Withdrawals	302
Bal.	600	

Truck Rental Expense	645
Bal.	230	

Advertising Expense	655
Bal.	75	

Fees Earned	401
	8,400	Bal.

Repairs Expense	684
Bal.	40	

Part 4 and analysis component: *Prepare these on the page provided for Part 4 and Analysis Component of Problem 3-9B.*

Problem 3-11B   Part 1

GENERAL JOURNAL   Page____

Date		Account Titles and Explanation	PR	Debit	Credit
Nov	1	Accounts Payable		10000	
		Cash			10000
	2	Office Equipment		34000	
		Cash			6000
		Notes Payable			28000
	3	Office Supplies		800	
		Cash			800
	4	no entry			

GENERAL JOURNAL   Page____

Date		Account Titles and Explanation	PR	Debit	Credit
	14	Wage Expense		6000	
		Cash			6000
	20	Cash		14000	
		Travel Revenue			14000
	25	Money withdrawal		2000	
		Cash			2000
		Interest Expense		150	
		Cash			150

Parts 2 and 3

	Cash	101	
Bal.	26,000	10000	
		6000	
		800	
		6000	
	14000	2000	
		150	
Bal	15050		

	Office Supplies	124	
Bal.	900	800	
	1700		

	Office Equipment	163	
Bal.	36,000		
	36000		
Bal	70000		

Accounts Payable   201

10000	43,000 Bal.
	33000

Notes Payable   205

	20,000 Bal.
	28000
	48000

Ike Petrov, Capital   301

	8,000 Bal.

Ike Petrov, Withdrawals   302

Bal. 4,000	
2000	
6000	

Travel Revenue   401

	34,000 Bal.
	14000
	48000 Bal

Wages Expense   623

Bal. 38,000	
6000	
46000	

Interest Expense   633

Bal. 100	
150	
250	

Part 4

Trial Balance

Income Statement

Statement of Changes in Equity

Balance Sheet

Analysis component:

_____
_____
_____
_____
_____
_____
_____
_____

Problem 3-12B

Income Statement

Statement of Changes in Equity

Balance Sheet

Trial Balance

Calculations:

Parts 2 and 6: October/November Transactions

GENERAL JOURNAL

Date		Account Titles and Explanation	PR	Debit	Credit

Name _____

Echo Systems (Cont'd.)

Date	Account Titles and Explanation	PR	Debit	Credit

Fundamental Accounting Principles, 13th Edition

Date	Account Titles and Explanation	PR	Debit	Credit

Cash   ACCOUNT NO. 101

DATE	EXPLANATION	PR	DEBIT	CREDIT	BALANCE

Accounts Receivable   ACCOUNT NO. 106

DATE	EXPLANATION	PR	DEBIT	CREDIT	BALANCE

Computer Supplies   ACCOUNT NO. 126

DATE	EXPLANATION	PR	DEBIT	CREDIT	BALANCE

Prepaid Insurance   ACCOUNT NO. 128

DATE	EXPLANATION	PR	DEBIT	CREDIT	BALANCE

Prepaid Rent   ACCOUNT NO. 131

DATE	EXPLANATION	PR	DEBIT	CREDIT	BALANCE

Office Equipment   ACCOUNT NO. 163

DATE	EXPLANATION	PR	DEBIT	CREDIT	BALANCE

Computer Equipment   ACCOUNT NO. 167

DATE	EXPLANATION	PR	DEBIT	CREDIT	BALANCE

Accounts Payable   ACCOUNT NO. 201

DATE	EXPLANATION	PR	DEBIT	CREDIT	BALANCE

Mary Graham, Capital   ACCOUNT NO. 301

DATE	EXPLANATION	PR	DEBIT	CREDIT	BALANCE

Mary Graham, Withdrawals   ACCOUNT NO. 302

DATE	EXPLANATION	PR	DEBIT	CREDIT	BALANCE

Computer Services Revenue   ACCOUNT NO. 403

DATE	EXPLANATION	PR	DEBIT	CREDIT	BALANCE

Wages Expense   ACCOUNT NO. 623

DATE	EXPLANATION	PR	DEBIT	CREDIT	BALANCE

Advertising Expense   ACCOUNT NO. 655

DATE	EXPLANATION	PR	DEBIT	CREDIT	BALANCE

Mileage Expense   ACCOUNT NO. 676

DATE	EXPLANATION	PR	DEBIT	CREDIT	BALANCE

Repairs Expense, Computer   ACCOUNT NO. 684

DATE	EXPLANATION	PR	DEBIT	CREDIT	BALANCE

Charitable Donations Expense   ACCOUNT NO. 699

DATE	EXPLANATION	PR	DEBIT	CREDIT	BALANCE

Part 4

ECHO SYSTMES
Trial Balance
October 31, 2011

	Debit	Credit

Part 5

ECHO SYSTEMS
Income Statement
Month Ended October 31, 2011

ECHO SYSTEMS
Statement of Changes in Equity
Month Ended October 31, 2011

ECHO SYSTEMS
Balance Sheet
October 31, 2011

Part 8

ECHO SYSTEMS
Trial Balance
November 30, 2011

	Debit	Credit

Part 9

ECHO SYSTEMS
Income Statement
For Two Months Ended November 30, 2011

ECHO SYSTEMS
Statement of Changes in Equity
For Two Months Ended November 30, 2011

ECHO SYSTEMS
Balance Sheet
November 30, 2011

  1. _____
     _____
     _____
  2. _____
     _____
     _____
  3. _____
     _____
     _____
  4. _____
     _____
     _____

Quick Study 4-2

Cash Basis: _____
_____
_____
_____

Accrual Basis: _____
_____
_____
_____
_____

Quick Study 4-3

GENERAL JOURNAL   Page____

Date	Account Titles and Explanation	PR	Debit	Credit
a.				
b.				
c.				

  d. _____
     _____

GENERAL JOURNAL   Page____

Date		Account Titles and Explanation	PR	Debit	Credit

Quick Study 4-5

GENERAL JOURNAL   Page____

Date		Account Titles and Explanation	PR	Debit	Credit

GENERAL JOURNAL   Page____

Date	Account Titles and Explanation	PR	Debit	Credit

Quick Study 4-7

GENERAL JOURNAL   Page____

Date	Account Titles and Explanation	PR	Debit	Credit

Quick Study 4-8

Debit	Credit	
a. _____	_____	Accrual of unpaid and unrecorded advertising that was used by Stark Company.
b. _____	_____	Adjustment of Unearned Services Revenue to recognize earned revenue.
c. _____	_____	Recorded revenue for work completed this accounting period; the cash will be received in the next period.
d. _____	_____	The cost of Equipment was matched to the time periods benefited.
e. _____	_____	Adjustment of Prepaid Advertising to recognize the portion used.

	Dr./Cr.	Account Titles	Statement
(a)	Debit		
	Credit		
(b)	Debit		
	Credit		
(c)	Debit		
	Credit		
(d)	Debit		
	Credit		
(e)	Debit		
	Credit		

Quick Study 4-10

		If adjustment is not recorded:			
	Type of Adjustment	Net income will be overstated, understated, or no effect	Assets will be overstated, understated, or no effect	Liabilities will be overstated, understated, or no effect	Equity will be overstated, understated, or no effect
a.	Prepaid Expenses				
b.	Depreciation				
c.	Unearned Revenues				
d.	Accrued Expenses				
e.	Accrued Revenues				

Quick Study 4-11

GENERAL JOURNAL   Page_____

Date	Account Titles and Explanation	PR	Debit	Credit

GENERAL JOURNAL

Page____

Date	Account Titles and Explanation	PR	Debit	Credit

*Quick Study 4-13

GENERAL JOURNAL

Page____

Date	Account Titles and Explanation	PR	Debit	Credit

GENERAL JOURNAL

Date	Account Titles and Explanation	PR	Debit	Credit
a.				
b.				
c.				
d.				

Name _____

Exercise 4-1

1. _____	7. _____
2. _____	8. _____
3. _____	9. _____
4. _____	10. _____
5. _____	11. _____
6. _____	12. _____

Exercise 4-2

GENERAL JOURNAL   Page____

Date	Account Titles and Explanation	PR	Debit	Credit
a.				
b.				
c.				
d.				
e.				
f.				
g.				

Name _____

GENERAL JOURNAL   Page____

Date	Account Titles and Explanation	PR	Debit	Credit
a.				
b.				
c.				
d.				
e.				
f.				
g.				

GENERAL JOURNAL   Page____

Date	Account Titles and Explanation	PR	Debit	Credit
a.				
b.				
c.				
d.				
e.				
f.				
g.				

GENERAL JOURNAL   Page____

Date	Account Titles and Explanation	PR	Debit	Credit
a.				
b.				
c.				

Exercise 4-6

GENERAL JOURNAL   Page____

Date	Account Titles and Explanation	PR	Debit	Credit
a.				
b.				
c.				
d.				
e.				

a. _____

_____

_____

_____

b. _____

_____

_____

_____

c. _____

_____

_____

_____

d. _____

_____

_____

_____

Exercise 4-8

Adjusting Entry:

GENERAL JOURNAL   Page____

Date	Account Titles and Explanation	PR	Debit	Credit

Payday Entry:

GENERAL JOURNAL   Page____

Date	Account Titles and Explanation	PR	Debit	Credit

Name _____

(a)
Adjusting Entry:

GENERAL JOURNAL   Page____

Date	Account Titles and Explanation	PR	Debit	Credit

Journal Entry (Next Period):

GENERAL JOURNAL   Page____

Date	Account Titles and Explanation	PR	Debit	Credit

(b)
Adjusting Entry:

GENERAL JOURNAL   Page____

Date	Account Titles and Explanation	PR	Debit	Credit

Journal Entry (Next Period):

GENERAL JOURNAL   Page____

Date	Account Titles and Explanation	PR	Debit	Credit

Fundamental Accounting Principles, 13th Edition

(c)
Adjusting Entry:

GENERAL JOURNAL   Page____

Date	Account Titles and Explanation	PR	Debit	Credit

Journal Entry (Next Period):

GENERAL JOURNAL   Page____

Date	Account Titles and Explanation	PR	Debit	Credit

Exercise 4-10

GENERAL JOURNAL   Page____

Date	Account Titles and Explanation	PR	Debit	Credit

GENERAL JOURNAL

Page____

Date	Account Titles and Explanation	PR	Debit	Credit

Analysis component:

_____

_____

_____

_____

_____

_____

ACCOUNT	UNADJUSTED TRIAL BALANCE		ADJUSTMENTS		ADJUSTED TRIAL BALANCE	
	Debit	Credit	Debit	Credit	Debit	Credit
Cash	5,000					
Accounts receivable	4,500					
Prepaid insurance	700					
Equipment	12,000					
Accum. deprec., equipment		6,000				
Accounts payable		1,200				
Abraham Nuna, capital		9,000				
Abraham Nuna, withdrawals	3,000					
Revenues		45,000				
Deprec. exp., equipment	-0-					
Salaries expense	29,000					
Insurance expense	7,000					
Totals	61,200	61,200				

Exercise 4-12

Income Statement

Statement of Changes in Equity

Balance Sheet

Analysis component:

_____
_____
_____
_____
_____
_____

*Exercise 4-13

GENERAL JOURNAL   Page____

Date	Account Titles and Explanation	PR	Debit	Credit
a.				
b.				

GENERAL JOURNAL   Page____

Date	Account Titles and Explanation	PR	Debit	Credit
c.				
d.				

Analysis component:

_____

_____

_____

_____

_____

_____

_____

GENERAL JOURNAL   Page____

Date	Account Titles and Explanation	PR	Debit	Credit
a.				
b.				
c.				
d.				
e.				
f.				

a. Initial credit recorded in Unearned Fees account:

GENERAL JOURNAL   Page____

Date	Account Titles and Explanation	PR	Debit	Credit

b. **Initial credit recorded in Fees Earned account:**

GENERAL JOURNAL   Page____

Date	Account Titles and Explanation	PR	Debit	Credit

c.

_____
_____
_____
_____
_____
_____
_____
_____

GENERAL JOURNAL   Page____

Date		Account Titles and Explanation	PR	Debit	Credit
a.					
b.					
c.					
d.					

Analysis component:

_____
_____
_____
_____

Problem 4-2A

GENERAL JOURNAL   Page____

Date		Account Titles and Explanation	PR	Debit	Credit
a.					
b.					
c.					

Analysis component:

_____
_____
_____
_____
_____
_____
_____
_____
_____

Problem 4-3A

GENERAL JOURNAL   Page____

Date	Account Titles and Explanation	PR	Debit	Credit
a.				
b.				
c.				
d.				

Analysis component:

_____
_____
_____
_____
_____
_____
_____

Adjusting Entries: **GENERAL JOURNAL**   Page_____

Date		Account Titles and Explanation	PR	Debit	Credit
a.					
Mar	31	Interest Expense		2250	
		Interest Payable			2250
		To record accrued interest			
b. Mar	31	Salaries Expense		19,600	
		Salaries Payable			19,600
		To record accrued s. exp.			
c.					
Mar	31	Telephone Expense		960	
		Accounts Payable			960
		To record acc telephone expense			
d.					
Mar	31	Rent Expense		5000	
		Rent Payable			3000
		To record acc. rent expense			
e.		Commission Expense		38400	
		Commission Payable			38400
		To record accrued commissions			

Subsequent Entries: **GENERAL JOURNAL**   Page____

Date		Account Titles and Explanation	PR	Debit	Credit
a.					
April	2	Interest Payable		2250	
		Cash			2250
		To record payment of ac. int.			
b.					
April	3	Salaries Payable		19,600	
		Salaries Expense		29,400	
		Cash			49,000
		To record pay. of solaries			
c.					
April	15	Accounts Payable		960	
		Cash			960
		To record pay. of accrual			
d.					
Apr.	26	Rent Payable		10000	
		Rent Expenses		5000	
		Prepaid Rent		15000	
		To record payment of rent 6 mo			30000
e.					
		Commissions Payable		38400	
		Cash			38400
		To record pay. accrued commi.			

Adjusting Entries: GENERAL JOURNAL   Page____

Date		Account Titles and Explanation	PR	Debit	Credit
a.					
mar	31	Rent Receivable		3,200	
		Rent Revenue			3,200
		To record accrued rev.			
b.					
Mar	31	Accounts Receivable		10,800	
		Service Revenue			10,800
		To record accrued revenue			
c.					
mar	31	Interest Receivable		700	
		Interest Revenue			700
		To record accrued int. revenue			
d.					
Mar	31	Accounts Receivable		8000	
		Service Rev			8000
		To record accrued ser revenues for Feb and Mar.			

Subsequent Entries: GENERAL JOURNAL   Page____

Date		Account Titles and Explanation	PR	Debit	Credit
a.					
Apr.	3	Cash		3200	
		Rent Rec			3200
		To record collection of accr.			
b.					
Apr	7	Cash		10,800	
		Accounts Receivable			10,800
c.					
April	1	Cash		700	
		Interest Rec.			700
		To record collec of acc. rev			
d.					
Apr	2	Cash		8000	
		Accounts Rec			8000
		To record coll of accrued rev.			

GENERAL JOURNAL   Page_____

Date		Account Titles and Explanation	PR	Debit	Credit
a.					
Dec	31	Insurance Expense		6000	
		Prepaid Insurance			6000
		To record the cost of insurance			
b.					
Dec	31	Teaching Supp. Expense		14800	
		Teaching Supplies			14800
		To record the cost of supplies.	20000 -5200		
c.					
	31	Depreciation Expense, Equip.		24000	
		Accumulated Depreciation			24000
		To record equip. depreciation expense			
d.					
	31	Depreciation Expense Lib		12000	
		Depreciation Prof Library			12000
e.					
	31	Unearned extension fees		8,800	
		Extension fees Earned			8,800
f.					
	31	Accounts Receivable		15000	
		Tuition Fees Earned			15000
		2,5/months = 15,000			
g.					
	31	Salaries Expense		800	
		Salaries Payable			800
		To record accrued salary			
		expense. 2 emp x 2 days = 800			
h.					
	31	Rent Expense		4000	
		Prepaid Rent			4000

Part 2: *See next page for Part 2 working paper.*

Part 3: _____

_____

_____

Part 4: _____

_____

_____

Part 2

ACCOUNT	UNADJUSTED TRIAL BALANCE Debit	UNADJUSTED TRIAL BALANCE Credit	ADJUSTMENTS Debit	ADJUSTMENTS Credit	ADJUSTED TRIAL BALANCE Debit	ADJUSTED TRIAL BALANCE Credit
Cash	52,000					
Accounts receivable	-0-		f) 15000			
Teaching supplies	20,000			b) 14800		
Prepaid insurance	30,000			a) 6000		
Prepaid rent	4,000			h) 4000		
Professional library	60,000					
Accum. deprec., library		18,000				
Equipment	140,000					
Accum. deprec., equipment		32,000		c) 24000		
Accounts payable		72,000				
Salaries payable		-0-		g) 800		
Unearned extension fees		22,000	e) 8800			
Karoo Ashevak, capital		127,200				
Karoo Ashevak, withdrwls	80,000					
Tuition fees earned		204,000		f) 15000		
Extension fees earned		76,000		e) 8800		
Deprec. exp., equipment	-0-		c) 24000			
Deprec. exp., library	-0-		d) 12000			
Salaries expense	96,000		g) 800			
Insurance expense	-0-		a) 6000			
Rent expense	44,000		h) 4000			
Teaching supplies expense	-0-		b) 14800			
Advertising expense	14,000					
Utilities expense	11,200					
Totals	551,200	551,200				

Problem 4-7A

Subsequent Entries: GENERAL JOURNAL   Page____

Date	Account Titles and Explanation	PR	Debit	Credit
a.				
Jan 31	Depreciation expense		1000	
	Accumulated Depreciation			1000
	To record depreciation			
b.				
	Unearned Consulting Fees		3,000	
	Unearned Con. Fees Earned			3,000
	To record fees earned			

GENERAL JOURNAL   Page____

Date		Account Titles and Explanation	PR	Debit	Credit
c.					
	31	Rent Expense		3,750	
		Pre paid Rent			3,750
d.	31	Wages Expense		9000	
		Wages Payable			9000
		To record accrued wages			
e.		Interest Expense		245	
		Interest Payable			245
		To record accrued Int.			
		Unrecorded Cons. Fees		4750	
f.		Unrecorded Cons. Fees Earned			4750
		To record accrued fees			
g.		Insurance Expense		75	
		Prepaid insurance			75
		To record expired insurance			
		1,350 / 18 = 75			
h.		Depreciation Expense, Equip.		450	
		Accumulated Depre.			450
		To rec. depreciation of off. fur.			
i.		Accounts Receivable		2050	
		Repair Rev. earned			2050
		To rec. accrued repair rev.			
j.		Store supplies expense		2150	
		Store supplies			2150
		To record store supplies used			
		800 + 1500 - 150 = 2150			

Part 1   GENERAL JOURNAL   Page____

Date	Account Titles and Explanation	PR	Debit	Credit

Part 2   **GENERAL JOURNAL**   Page____

Date		Account Titles and Explanation	PR	Debit	Credit

Chapter 4   Problem 4-9A

GENERAL JOURNAL   Page____

Date		Account Titles and Explanation	PR	Debit	Credit
a.		Unearned Consulting Fees		1160	
		Consulting Fees Earned			1160
		To record fees earned			
b.		Consulting Fees Earned		6000	
		Unearned Consulting Fees			6000
c.		Rent Expense		14000	
		Prepaid Rent			14000
		21000-7000 = 14000			
d.		Wages Expense		16800	
		Wages Payable			16800

March 1 2012 ↓ ↓ *20*   *24 months*   *12/8*
6 months

GENERAL JOURNAL   Page____

Date	Account Titles and Explanation	PR	Debit	Credit
e.	Depreciation Expense, Furn-		13653	
	Accumulated Depreciation			13.653
	8 months = 26480			
f.	Accounts Receivable		4200	
	Consulting Fees Earned			4200
g.	Notes Receivable		200	
	Interest Receivable			200
h.	Insurance Expense		7402	
	Prepaid Insurance			7402
	9350 ÷ .19/24 = 7402			
i.	Supplies Expense		900	
	Supplies			900

Problem 4-10A   Parts 1 and 2

GENERAL LEDGER

Cash   **ACCOUNT NO. 101**

DATE	EXPLANATION	PR	DEBIT	CREDIT	BALANCE
2011					
Oct. 31	Balance				28,000

Accounts Receivable   **ACCOUNT NO. 106**

DATE	EXPLANATION	PR	DEBIT	CREDIT	BALANCE
2011					
Oct. 31	Balance				56,000
			4200		60200

Interest Receivable   ACCOUNT NO. 109

DATE	EXPLANATION	PR	DEBIT	CREDIT	BALANCE
2011					
				200	200

Notes Receivable   ACCOUNT NO. 111

DATE	EXPLANATION	PR	DEBIT	CREDIT	BALANCE
2011					
Oct. 31	Balance			200	30,000

Supplies   ACCOUNT NO. 126

DATE	EXPLANATION	PR	DEBIT	CREDIT	BALANCE
2011					
Oct. 31	Balance				4,600
				200	3500

Prepaid Insurance   ACCOUNT NO. 128

DATE	EXPLANATION	PR	DEBIT	CREDIT	BALANCE
2011					
Oct. 31	Balance				9,350
				7402	1948

Prepaid Rent   ACCOUNT NO. 131

DATE	EXPLANATION	PR	DEBIT	CREDIT	BALANCE
2011					
Oct. 31	Balance				21,000
				14100	7000

Office Furniture   ACCOUNT NO. 161

DATE	EXPLANATION	PR	DEBIT	CREDIT	BALANCE
2011					
Oct. 31	Balance			13553	61,440

Accumulated Depreciation, Office Furniture   ACCOUNT NO. 162

DATE	EXPLANATION	PR	DEBIT	CREDIT	BALANCE
2011					
Oct. 31	Balance				20,480
				13653	

Accounts Payable　　　ACCOUNT NO. 201

DATE	EXPLANATION	PR	DEBIT	CREDIT	BALANCE
2011					
Oct. 31	Balance				35,000

Wages Payable　　　ACCOUNT NO. 210

DATE	EXPLANATION	PR	DEBIT	CREDIT	BALANCE
2011					
					6800

Unearned Consulting Fees　　　ACCOUNT NO. 233

DATE	EXPLANATION	PR	DEBIT	CREDIT	BALANCE
2011					
Oct. 31	Balance				13,160
			1160	1	
				6000	18000

Jeff Moore, Capital　　　ACCOUNT NO. 301

DATE	EXPLANATION	PR	DEBIT	CREDIT	BALANCE
2011					
Oct. 31	Balance				60,000

Jeff Moore, Withdrawals　　　ACCOUNT NO. 302

DATE	EXPLANATION	PR	DEBIT	CREDIT	BALANCE
2011					
Oct. 31	Balance				16,450

Consulting Fees Earned　　　ACCOUNT NO. 401

DATE	EXPLANATION	PR	DEBIT	CREDIT	BALANCE
2011					
Oct. 31	Balance				314,600
				1160	
			6000		
					209760

Interest Revenue   ACCOUNT NO. 409

DATE	EXPLANATION	PR	DEBIT	CREDIT	BALANCE
2011					
Oct. 31	Balance				1,400

Depreciation Expense, Office Furniture   ACCOUNT NO. 601

DATE	EXPLANATION	PR	DEBIT	CREDIT	BALANCE
2011					
					13653

Wages Expense   ACCOUNT NO. 622

DATE	EXPLANATION	PR	DEBIT	CREDIT	BALANCE
2011					
Oct. 31	Balance				147,000
				6800	

Insurance Expense   ACCOUNT NO. 637

DATE	EXPLANATION	PR	DEBIT	CREDIT	BALANCE
2011					
					7402

Rent Expense   ACCOUNT NO. 640

DATE	EXPLANATION	PR	DEBIT	CREDIT	BALANCE
2011					
Oct. 31	Balance				64,000
				14000	78000

Supplies Expense   ACCOUNT NO. 650

DATE	EXPLANATION	PR	DEBIT	CREDIT	BALANCE
2011					
Oct. 31	Balance				6,800
				500	

Adjusted Trial Balance

	Cash	28000	
	Ac. Receivable	60,200	
~	In. Receivable	200	200
	Notes Receivable	29800	
	Supplies	3500	
	Prepard Insurance	1948	
	Prepaid Rent	7000	
	Off Furniture	61440	
~	Accum Depreciation		34.133
	Accounts Payable		35000
	Wages Payable		6800
	Unearned Cons Fees		18000
	Capital		60000
	Withdrawal	16450	
	Interest Revenue		1400
	Consulting Fees Earned		309760
	Wages Expense	153800	
	Insurance Expense	7402	
	Rent Expense	78000	
	Supplies Expense	7700	

Part 4   455440   465093

Income Statement

Statement of Changes in Equity

Balance Sheet

Analysis component:

GENERAL JOURNAL

Page____

Date	Account Titles and Explanation	PR	Debit	Credit
a.				
b.				
c.				
d.				
e.				
f.				
g.				

ACCOUNT	UNADJUSTED TRIAL BALANCE		ADJUSTMENTS		ADJUSTED TRIAL BALANCE	
	Debit	Credit	Debit	Credit	Debit	Credit
Cash	6,000					
Accounts receivable	11,200					
Repair supplies	2,200					
Prepaid rent	14,000					
Office furniture	26,000					
Accounts payable		8,000				
Notes payable		21,600				
Eli Arrow, capital		67,758				
Eli Arrow, withdrawals	5,000					
Hospitality revenues		128,000				
Salaries expense	144,000					
Wages expense	16,958					
Totals	225,358	225,358				

Part 2

Income Statement

Statement of Changes in Equity

Balance Sheet

Analysis component:

Income Statement

Statement of Changes in Equity

Balance Sheet

Analysis component:

GENERAL JOURNAL

Page____

Date	Account Titles and Explanation	PR	Debit	Credit

Cash	101

Prepaid Rent	131

Office Furniture	161

Accum. Deprec., Office Furn.	162

Accounts Payable	201

Unearned Revenue	233

Delanie Tugut, Capital	301

Delanie Tugut, Withdrawals	302

Revenue 401

Deprec. Exp., Office Furniture	602

Wages Expense	623

Rent Expense	640

Telephone Expense	688

Hotel Expenses	696

Part 4

Trial Balance

	Debit	Credit

Part 5 – Adjusting entries

GENERAL JOURNAL   Page____

Date	Account Titles and Explanation	PR	Debit	Credit

Part 6

Trial Balance

	Debit	Credit

Part 7

Income Statement

Part 7 (concl'd.)

Statement of Changes in Equity

Balance Sheet

Analysis component:

GENERAL JOURNAL   Page____

Date	Account Titles and Explanation	PR	Debit	Credit

Analysis component:

_____
_____
_____
_____
_____
_____
_____
_____

ACCOUNT	UNADJUSTED TRIAL BALANCE		ADJUSTMENTS		ADJUSTED TRIAL BALANCE	
	Debit	Credit	Debit	Credit	Debit	Credit
Cash	20,000					
Accounts receivable	49,700					
Prepaid rent	-0-					
Prepaid insurance	-0-					
Accounts payable		2,500				
Unearned consulting fees		-0-				
Bruce Willis, capital		15,600				
Consulting fees earned		82,000				
Rent expense	28,000					
Insurance expense	2,400					
Totals	100,100	100,100				

*Problem 4-17A

Part 1 - Entries that initially recognize assets and liabilities:

GENERAL JOURNAL   Page____

Date		Account Titles and Explanation	PR	Debit	Credit

GENERAL JOURNAL   Page____

Date	Account Titles and Explanation	PR	Debit	Credit

Part 2 – Entries that initially recognize expenses and revenues:

GENERAL JOURNAL   Page___

Date	Account Titles and Explanation	PR	Debit	Credit

Part 2 (concluded)

GENERAL JOURNAL   Page____

Date	Account Titles and Explanation	PR	Debit	Credit

Analysis component:

_____
_____
_____
_____
_____
_____
_____
_____
_____
_____
_____
_____
_____
_____
_____

GENERAL JOURNAL   Page____

Date	Account Titles and Explanation	PR	Debit	Credit
a.				
b.				
c.				
d.				

Analysis component:

_____

_____

_____

_____

Problem 4-2B

GENERAL JOURNAL   Page____

Date	Account Titles and Explanation	PR	Debit	Credit
a.				
b.				
c.				

Analysis component: _____

_____

_____

_____

_____

_____

_____

_____

_____

Problem 4-3B

GENERAL JOURNAL   Page____

Date	Account Titles and Explanation	PR	Debit	Credit
a.				
b.				
c.				
d.				

Analysis component: _____

_____

_____

_____

_____

_____

_____

_____

Adjusting Entries: **GENERAL JOURNAL**   Page____

Date	Account Titles and Explanation	PR	Debit	Credit
a.				
b.				
c.				
d.				
e.				

Subsequent Entries: GENERAL JOURNAL   Page____

Date	Account Titles and Explanation	PR	Debit	Credit
a.				
b.				
c.				
d.				
e.				

Adjusting Entries: **GENERAL JOURNAL**   Page____

Date	Account Titles and Explanation	PR	Debit	Credit
a.				
b.				
c.				
d.				

Subsequent Entries: **GENERAL JOURNAL**   Page____

Date	Account Titles and Explanation	PR	Debit	Credit
a.				
b.				
c.				
d.				

GENERAL JOURNAL   Page____

Date	Account Titles and Explanation	PR	Debit	Credit
a.				
b.				
c.				
d.				
e.				
f.				
g.				
h.				

Part 2: *See next page for Part 2 working paper.*

Part 3: _____

_____

_____

Part 4: _____

_____

_____

_____

Part 2

ACCOUNT	UNADJUSTED TRIAL BALANCE Debit	Credit	ADJUSTMENTS Debit	Credit	ADJUSTED TRIAL BALANCE Debit	Credit
Cash	100,000					
Accounts receivable	-0-					
Teaching supplies	120,000					
Prepaid insurance	36,000					
Prepaid rent	5,200					
Professional library	20,000					
Accum. deprec., library		3,000				
Equipment	60,000					
Accum. deprec., equipment		32,000				
Accounts payable		24,400				
Salaries payable		-0-				
Unearned extension fees		55,200				
Jay Fawcett, capital		137,000				
Jay Fawcett, withdrawals	40,000					
Tuition fees earned		210,000				
Extension fees earned		124,000				
Deprec. exp., equipment	-0-					
Deprec. exp., library	-0-					
Salaries expense	143,600					
Insurance expense	-0-					
Rent expense	-0-					
Teaching supplies expense	-0-					
Advertising expense	36,000					
Utilities expense	24,800					
Totals	585,600	585,600				

Problem 4-7B

Subsequent Entries: **GENERAL JOURNAL**   Page____

Date	Account Titles and Explanation	PR	Debit	Credit
a.				
b.				

GENERAL JOURNAL   Page____

Date	Account Titles and Explanation	PR	Debit	Credit
c.				
d.				
e.				
f.				
g.				
h.				
i.				
j.				

Name _____

Part 1   GENERAL JOURNAL   Page____

Date	Account Titles and Explanation	PR	Debit	Credit

Part 2   **GENERAL JOURNAL**   Page____

Date	Account Titles and Explanation	PR	Debit	Credit

Chapter 4   Problem 4-9B

GENERAL JOURNAL   Page____

Date	Account Titles and Explanation	PR	Debit	Credit
a.				
b.				
c.				
d.				

GENERAL JOURNAL

Page____

Date	Account Titles and Explanation	PR	Debit	Credit
e.				
f.				
g.				
h.				
i.				

Analysis component:

_____

_____

_____

_____

_____

_____

_____

_____

_____

_____

Name _____

Parts 1 and 2

Cash   ACCOUNT NO. 101

DATE	EXPLANATION	PR	DEBIT	CREDIT	BALANCE
2011					
Dec. 31	Balance				5,600

Accounts Receivable   ACCOUNT NO. 106

DATE	EXPLANATION	PR	DEBIT	CREDIT	BALANCE
2011					
Dec. 31	Balance				7,910

Supplies   ACCOUNT NO. 126

DATE	EXPLANATION	PR	DEBIT	CREDIT	BALANCE
2011					
					640

Prepaid Advertising   ACCOUNT NO. 128

DATE	EXPLANATION	PR	DEBIT	CREDIT	BALANCE
2011					
Dec. 31	Balance				5,600

Prepaid Rent   ACCOUNT NO. 131

DATE	EXPLANATION	PR	DEBIT	CREDIT	BALANCE
2011					
Dec. 31	Balance				27,000

Surveying Equipment   ACCOUNT NO. 167

DATE	EXPLANATION	PR	DEBIT	CREDIT	BALANCE
2011					
Dec. 31	Balance				58,000

Accum. Deprec. – Surveying Equipment   ACCOUNT NO. 168

DATE	EXPLANATION	PR	DEBIT	CREDIT	BALANCE
2011					
Dec. 31	Balance				7,348

Fundamental Accounting Principles, 13th Edition

Accounts Payable   ACCOUNT NO. 201

DATE	EXPLANATION	PR	DEBIT	CREDIT	BALANCE
2011					
Dec. 31	Balance				3,800

Interest Payable   ACCOUNT NO. 203

DATE	EXPLANATION	PR	DEBIT	CREDIT	BALANCE
2011					

Wages Payable   ACCOUNT NO. 210

DATE	EXPLANATION	PR	DEBIT	CREDIT	BALANCE
2011					

Unearned Surveying Fees   ACCOUNT NO. 233

DATE	EXPLANATION	PR	DEBIT	CREDIT	BALANCE
2011					
Dec. 31	Balance				4,800

Notes Payable   ACCOUNT NO. 251

DATE	EXPLANATION	PR	DEBIT	CREDIT	BALANCE
2011					
Dec. 31	Balance				36,000

Ben Hallmark, Capital   ACCOUNT NO. 301

DATE	EXPLANATION	PR	DEBIT	CREDIT	BALANCE
2011					
Dec. 31	Balance				28,652

Ben Hallmark, Withdrawals   ACCOUNT NO. 302

DATE	EXPLANATION	PR	DEBIT	CREDIT	BALANCE
2011					
Dec. 31	Balance				4,300

Surveying Fees Earned   ACCOUNT NO. 401

DATE	EXPLANATION	PR	DEBIT	CREDIT	BALANCE
2011					
Dec. 31	Balance				134,098

Depreciation Expense, Surveying Equipment   ACCOUNT NO. 601

DATE	EXPLANATION	PR	DEBIT	CREDIT	BALANCE
2011					

Salaries Expense   ACCOUNT NO. 622

DATE	EXPLANATION	PR	DEBIT	CREDIT	BALANCE
2011					
Dec. 31	Balance				38,000

Wages Expense   ACCOUNT NO. 623

DATE	EXPLANATION	PR	DEBIT	CREDIT	BALANCE
2011					
Dec. 31	Balance				39,726

Interest Expense   ACCOUNT NO. 633

DATE	EXPLANATION	PR	DEBIT	CREDIT	BALANCE
2011					

Insurance Expense   ACCOUNT NO. 637

DATE	EXPLANATION	PR	DEBIT	CREDIT	BALANCE
2011					
Dec. 31	Balance				6,000

Rent Expense   ACCOUNT NO. 640

DATE	EXPLANATION	PR	DEBIT	CREDIT	BALANCE
2011					

Supplies Expense — ACCOUNT NO. 650

DATE	EXPLANATION	PR	DEBIT	CREDIT	BALANCE
2011					
Dec. 31	Balance				2,958

Advertising Expense — ACCOUNT NO. 655

DATE	EXPLANATION	PR	DEBIT	CREDIT	BALANCE
2011					

Gas and Oil Expense — ACCOUNT NO. 671

DATE	EXPLANATION	PR	DEBIT	CREDIT	BALANCE
2011					
Dec. 31	Balance				6,564

Repairs Expense — ACCOUNT NO. 684

DATE	EXPLANATION	PR	DEBIT	CREDIT	BALANCE
2011					
Dec. 31	Balance				12,400

Utilities Expense — ACCOUNT NO. 690

DATE	EXPLANATION	PR	DEBIT	CREDIT	BALANCE
2011					

Adjusted Trial Balance

Income Statement

Statement of Changes in Equity

Balance Sheet

Analysis component:

_____

_____

_____

_____

_____

_____

_____

_____

_____

GENERAL JOURNAL

Date	Account Titles and Explanation	PR	Debit	Credit
a.				
b.				
c.				
d.				
e.				
f.				
g.				

ACCOUNT	UNADJUSTED TRIAL BALANCE		ADJUSTMENTS		ADJUSTED TRIAL BALANCE	
	Debit	Credit	Debit	Credit	Debit	Credit
Cash	112,000					
Accounts receivable	28,000					
Repair supplies	2,800					
Prepaid arena rental	182,000					
Skate equipment	428,000					
Accum. deprec., skate eq.		164,000				
Accounts payable		5,400				
Unearned training fees		19,600				
Notes payable		160,000				
Ben Gibson, capital		451,400				
Ben Gibson, withdrawals	72,000					
Training fees earned		550,000				
Salaries expense	350,000					
Arena rental expense	168,000					
Other expenses	7,600					
Totals	1,350,400	1,350,400				

Part 2

Income Statement

Statement of Changes in Equity

Balance Sheet

Analysis component:

_____

_____

_____

_____

_____

_____

_____

Income Statement

Statement of Changes in Equity

Balance Sheet

GENERAL JOURNAL   Page____

Date	Account Titles and Explanation	PR	Debit	Credit

Parts 2, 3, and 5

	Cash	101
Bal.	6,400	

	Repair Supplies	131
Bal.	3,000	

	Tools	161
Bal.	16,800	

Accum. Deprec., Tools		162
	560	Bal.

Accounts Payable		201
	3,200	Bal.

Unearned Revenue		233
	700	Bal.

Melanie Thornhill, Capital		301
	9,160	Bal.

Melanie Thornhill, Withdrawals		302
Bal.	-0-	

Revenue 401		
	25,800	Bal.

	Deprec. Exp., Tools	602
Bal.	560	

	Wages Expense	623
Bal.	1,960	

	Rent Expense	640
Bal.	8,000	

	Repairs Supplies Expense	696
Bal.	2,700	

Part 4

Trial Balance

	Debit	Credit

Part 5 – Adjusting entries

GENERAL JOURNAL   Page____

Date	Account Titles and Explanation	PR	Debit	Credit

Part 6

Trial Balance

	Debit	Credit

Part 7

Income Statement

Part 6 (concl'd.)

Statement of Changes in Equity

Balance Sheet

Analysis component:

GENERAL JOURNAL   Page____

Date	Account Titles and Explanation	PR	Debit	Credit

Analysis component:

_____
_____
_____
_____
_____
_____
_____
_____

ACCOUNT	UNADJUSTED TRIAL BALANCE		ADJUSTMENTS		ADJUSTED TRIAL BALANCE	
	Debit	Credit	Debit	Credit	Debit	Credit
Cash	14,500					
Accounts receivable	9,000					
Prepaid advertising	-0-					
Cleaning supplies	-0-					
Equipment	31,000					
Accum. deprec., equipment		1,500				
Unearned window washing fees		-0-				
Unearned office cleaning fees		-0-				
William Nahanee, capital		9,150				
Window washing fees earned		38,000				
Office cleaning fees earned		69,000				
Advertising expense	3,650					
Salaries expense	48,500					
Depreciation expense, equip.	-0-					
Cleaning supplies expense	11,000					
Totals	117,650	117,650				

*Problem 4-17B

Part 1 - Entries that initially recognize assets and liabilities:

GENERAL JOURNAL   Page____

Date	Account Titles and Explanation	PR	Debit	Credit

GENERAL JOURNAL   Page____

Date	Account Titles and Explanation	PR	Debit	Credit

Part 2 – Entries that initially recognize expenses and revenues:

GENERAL JOURNAL   Page____

Date	Account Titles and Explanation	PR	Debit	Credit

Part 2 (concl'd)

GENERAL JOURNAL   Page____

Date	Account Titles and Explanation	PR	Debit	Credit

Analysis component:

_____
_____
_____
_____
_____
_____
_____
_____
_____
_____
_____
_____
_____
_____
_____

GENERAL JOURNAL   Page _____

Date	Account Titles and Explanation	PR	Debit	Credit

Date	Account Titles and Explanation	PR	Debit	Credit

GENERAL LEDGER

Cash   ACCOUNT NO. 101

DATE	EXPLANATION	PR	DEBIT	CREDIT	BALANCE
2011 Nov. 30	Balance				70,340

Accounts Receivable   ACCOUNT NO. 106

DATE	EXPLANATION	PR	DEBIT	CREDIT	BALANCE
2011 Nov. 30	Balance				18,900

Computer Supplies   ACCOUNT NO. 126

DATE	EXPLANATION	PR	DEBIT	CREDIT	BALANCE
2011 Nov. 30	Balance				4,560

Prepaid Insurance   ACCOUNT NO. 128

DATE	EXPLANATION	PR	DEBIT	CREDIT	BALANCE
2011 Nov. 30	Balance				4,320

Prepaid Rent   ACCOUNT NO. 131

DATE	EXPLANATION	PR	DEBIT	CREDIT	BALANCE
2011 Nov. 30	Balance				9,000

Office Equipment — ACCOUNT NO. 163

DATE	EXPLANATION	PR	DEBIT	CREDIT	BALANCE
2011 Nov. 30	Balance				18,000

Accumulated Depreciation, Office Equipment — ACCOUNT NO. 164

DATE	EXPLANATION	PR	DEBIT	CREDIT	BALANCE
2011 Nov. 30	Balance				-0-

Computer Equipment — ACCOUNT NO. 167

DATE	EXPLANATION	PR	DEBIT	CREDIT	BALANCE
2011 Nov. 30	Balance				36,000

Accumulated Depreciation, Computer Equipment — ACCOUNT NO. 168

DATE	EXPLANATION	PR	DEBIT	CREDIT	BALANCE
2011 Nov. 30	Balance				-0-

Accounts Payable — ACCOUNT NO. 201

DATE	EXPLANATION	PR	DEBIT	CREDIT	BALANCE
2011 Nov. 30	Balance				-0-

Wages Payable — ACCOUNT NO. 210

DATE	EXPLANATION	PR	DEBIT	CREDIT	BALANCE
2011 Nov. 30	Balance				-0-

Unearned Computer Services Revenue — ACCOUNT NO. 236

DATE	EXPLANATION	PR	DEBIT	CREDIT	BALANCE
2011 Nov. 30	Balance				-0-

Mary Graham, Capital — ACCOUNT NO. 301

DATE	EXPLANATION	PR	DEBIT	CREDIT	BALANCE
2011 Nov. 30	Balance				144,000

Part 2   Echo Systems (Cont'd.)

Mary Graham, Withdrawals   ACCOUNT NO. 302

DATE	EXPLANATION	PR	DEBIT	CREDIT	BALANCE
2011 Nov. 30	Balance				10,800

Computer Services Revenue   ACCOUNT NO. 403

DATE	EXPLANATION	PR	DEBIT	CREDIT	BALANCE
2011 Nov. 30	Balance				40,950

Depreciation Expense, Office Equipment   ACCOUNT NO. 612

DATE	EXPLANATION	PR	DEBIT	CREDIT	BALANCE
2011 Nov. 30	Balance				-0-

Depreciation Expense, Computer Equipment   ACCOUNT NO. 613

DATE	EXPLANATION	PR	DEBIT	CREDIT	BALANCE
2011 Nov. 30	Balance				-0-

Wages Expense   ACCOUNT NO. 623

DATE	EXPLANATION	PR	DEBIT	CREDIT	BALANCE
2011 Nov. 30	Balance				4,200

Insurance Expense   ACCOUNT NO. 637

DATE	EXPLANATION	PR	DEBIT	CREDIT	BALANCE
2011 Nov. 30	Balance				-0-

Rent Expense   ACCOUNT NO. 640

DATE	EXPLANATION	PR	DEBIT	CREDIT	BALANCE
2011 Nov. 30	Balance				-0-

Part 2   Echo Systems (Cont'd.)

Computer Supplies Expense — ACCOUNT NO. 652

DATE	EXPLANATION	PR	DEBIT	CREDIT	BALANCE
2011 Nov. 30	Balance				-0-

Advertising Expense — ACCOUNT NO. 655

DATE	EXPLANATION	PR	DEBIT	CREDIT	BALANCE
2011 Nov. 30	Balance				3,720

Mileage Expense — ACCOUNT NO. 676

DATE	EXPLANATION	PR	DEBIT	CREDIT	BALANCE
2011 Nov. 30	Balance				2,200

Repairs Expense, Computer — ACCOUNT NO. 684

DATE	EXPLANATION	PR	DEBIT	CREDIT	BALANCE
2011 Nov. 30	Balance				1,410

Charitable Donations Expense — ACCOUNT NO. 699

DATE	EXPLANATION	PR	DEBIT	CREDIT	BALANCE
2011 Nov. 30	Balance				1,500

ECHO SYSTEMS
Adjusted Trial Balance
December 31, 2011

	Debit	Credit

ECHO SYSTEMS
Income Statement
For Three Months Ended December 31, 2011

Part 5

ECHO SYSTEMS
Statement of Changes in Equity
For Three Months Ended December 31, 2011

ECHO SYSTEMS
Balance Sheet
December 31, 2011

Name _____

1. _____Equipment   4. _____Prepaid insurance
2. _____Owner, withdrawals   5. _____Accounts receivable
3. _____Insurance expense   6. _____Depreciation expense, equipment

Quick Study 5-2

- see next page for QS 5-2 working paper

Quick Study 5-3

_____
_____
_____
_____
_____
_____
_____
_____
_____

Quick Study 5-4

_____
_____
_____
_____
_____
_____
_____
_____

Quick Study 5-5

_____
_____
_____
_____
_____
_____
_____
_____
_____
_____
_____
_____

Fundamental Accounting Principles, 13th Edition

Account Title	Unadjusted Trial Balance		Adjustments		Adjusted Trial Balance		Income Statement		Balance Sheet & Statement of Changes in Equity	
	Debit	Credit	Debit	Credit	Debit	Credit	Debit	Credit	Debit	Credit
Cash	15									
Accounts receivable	22									
Supplies	25			8						
Ed Wolt, capital		40								
Ed Wolt, withdrawals	12									
Fees earned		48								
Supplies expense		—	8	—						
Totals	88	88	8	8						

GENERAL JOURNAL   Page____

Date	Account Titles and Explanation	PR	Debit	Credit

Assets	Liabilities
250	30

Capital	Withdrawals
200	20

	Expenses
Revenue	60
100	

| | Income Summary |

GENERAL JOURNAL   Page____

Date	Account Titles and Explanation	PR	Debit	Credit

Assets	Liabilities
250	110

Capital	Withdrawals
200	20

Revenue	Expenses
100	140

Income Summary

Post-Closing Trial Balance

	Debit	Credit

Quick Study 5-9

a. _____ Preparing the unadjusted trial balance.
b. _____ Preparing the post-closing trial balance.
c. _____ Journalizing and posting adjusting entries.
d. _____ Journalizing and posting closing entries.
e. _____ Preparing the financial statements.
f. _____ Journalizing transactions.
g. _____ Posting the transaction entries.
h. _____ Completing the work sheet.

Quick Study 5-10

1. _____ Store equipment
2. _____ Wages payable
3. _____ Cash
4. _____ Notes payable (due in three years)
5. _____ Land not currently used in business operations
6. _____ Accounts receivable
7. _____ Trademarks

1. ____ Depreciation expense, trucks
2. ____ Lee Hale, capital
3. ____ Interest receivable
4. ____ Lee Hale, withdrawals
5. ____ Automobiles
6. ____ Notes payable (due in 3 years)
7. ____ Accounts payable
8. ____ Prepaid insurance
9. ____ Land not currently used in business operations
10. ____ Unearned services revenue
11. ____ Accum. deprec., trucks
12. ____ Cash
13. ____ Building
14. ____ Patent
15. ____ Office equipment
16. ____ Land (used in operations)
17. ____ Repairs expense
18. ____ Prepaid property taxes
19. ____ Notes payable (due in 2 months)
20. ____ Notes receivable (due in 2 years)

Quick Study 5-12

Partial Balance Sheet

*Quick Study 5-13

GENERAL JOURNAL   Page____

Date	Account Titles and Explanation	PR	Debit	Credit

_____
_____
_____
_____

Exercise 5-1

1. _____ Roberta Jefferson, withdrawals
2. _____ Interest earned
3. _____ Accum. deprec., machinery
4. _____ Service fees revenue
5. _____ Accounts receivable
6. _____ Rent expense
7. _____ Deprec. exp., machinery
8. _____ Accounts payable

9. _____ Cash
10. _____ Office supplies
11. _____ Roberta Jefferson, capital
12. _____ Wages payable
13. _____ Machinery
14. _____ Insurance expense
15. _____ Interest expense
16. _____ Interest receivable

Exercise 5-2

ACCOUNT	ADJUSTED TRIAL BALANCE Debit	ADJUSTED TRIAL BALANCE Credit	INCOME STATEMENT Debit	INCOME STATEMENT Credit	BALANCE SHEET AND STATEMENT OF CHANGES IN EQUITY Debit	BALANCE SHEET AND STATEMENT OF CHANGES IN EQUITY Credit
Cash	3,000					
Accounts receivable	13,100					
Trucks	41,000					
Accum. deprec., trucks		16,500				
Franchise	15,000					
Accounts payable		7,000				
Salaries payable		1,600				
Unearned fees		1,300				
Bo Webber, capital		37,750				
Bo Webber, withdrls.	7,200					
Plumbing fees earned		49,000				
Deprec. expense, trucks	5,500					
Salaries expense	18,500					
Rent expense	6,000					
Miscellaneous expense	3,850					
Totals	113,150	113,150				

Parts 1, 2, and 3

Musical Sensations

Work Sheet

For Year Ended December 31, 2011

Account Title	Unadjusted Trial Balance		Adjustments		Adjusted Trial Balance		Income Statement		Balance Sheet and Statement of Changes in Equity	
	Debit	Credit	Debit	Credit	Debit	Credit	Debit	Credit	Debit	Credit
Cash	14,000									
Accounts receivable	26,000									
Office supplies	950									
Musical equipment	212,000									
Accum. dep., musical equip.		16,200								
Accounts payable		3,350								
Unearned performance rev.		12,400								
Jim Daley, capital		272,000								
Jim Daley, withdrawals	52,000									
Performance revenue		119,000								
Salaries expense	76,000									
Travelling expense	42,000									
Totals	422,950	422,950								

Part 4

_____

_____   **Jim Daley, Capital**
_____   _____|_____
_____ |
_____ |
_____ |

Exercise 5-4

1(a) _____

2(a)   **GENERAL JOURNAL**   Page____

Date	Account Titles and Explanation	PR	Debit	Credit

3(a)   **Owner's Capital**
                                        _____|_____
_____ |
_____ |
_____ |
_____ |

1(b) _____

2(b)   **GENERAL JOURNAL**   Page____

Date	Account Titles and Explanation	PR	Debit	Credit

3(b)   **Owner's Capital**
                                        _____|_____
_____ |
_____ |
_____ |

	Debit	Credit
Rent earned		99,000
Salaries expense	35,300	
Insurance expense	4,400	
Dock rental expense	12,000	
Boat supplies expense	6,220	
Depreciation expense, boats	21,500	
Totals		
Net income		
Totals		

Closing Entries

GENERAL JOURNAL   Page____

Date	Account Titles and Explanation	PR	Debit	Credit

GENERAL JOURNAL   Page____

Date	Account Titles and Explanation	PR	Debit	Credit

Post-Closing Trial Balance

	Debit	Credit

GENERAL JOURNAL

Page____

Date	Account Titles and Explanation	PR	Debit	Credit

Exercise 5-8

GENERAL JOURNAL

Page____

Date	Account Titles and Explanation	PR	Debit	Credit

GENERAL JOURNAL

Page____

Date	Account Titles and Explanation	PR	Debit	Credit

Exercise 5-10

GENERAL JOURNAL

Page____

Date	Account Titles and Explanation	PR	Debit	Credit

Posting to Accounts:

Assets		Liabilities	
Bal. Dec. 31 **80,000**			**38,100** Bal. Dec. 31

Marcy Jones, Capital		Marcy Jones, Withdrawals	
	41,000 Bal. Dec. 31	Bal. Dec. 31 **24,000**	

Services Revenue		Salaries Expense	
	73,000 Bal. Dec. 31	Bal. Dec. 31 **20,000**	

Rent Expense		Insurance Expense	
Bal. Dec. 31 **8,600**		Bal. Dec. 31 **3,500**	

Depreciation Expense		Income Summary	
Bal. Dec. 31 **16,000**			

Exercise 5-11

Post-Closing Trial Balance

	Debit	Credit

1. _____

2.   GENERAL JOURNAL   Page____

Date	Account Titles and Explanation	PR	Debit	Credit

3.   Bill Duggan, Capital

_____ |
_____ |
_____ |
_____ |

Exercise 5-13

a.

Account Title	Adjusted Trial Balance Debit	Credit
Accounts payable		$ 11,000
Accounts receivable	$ 59,000	
Accumulated depreciation, equipment		9,000
Accumulated depreciation, truck..		21,000
Cash...	29,000	
Depreciation expense..	3,800	
Equipment..	13,000	
Franchise	17,800	
Gas and oil expense	7,500	
Interest expense..	4,500	
Interest payable...		750
Land not currently used in business operations.................	52,000	
Long-term notes payable		35,000
Notes payable, due February 1, 2012		7,000
Notes receivable..	6,000	
Patent...	7,000	
Prepaid Rent	14,000	
Rent expense...	39,000	
Repair revenue		247,000
Repair supplies	17,000	
Repair supplies expense..	14,000	
Sid Whimsly, capital		24,050
Sid Whimsly, withdrawals..	49,000	
Truck...	26,000	
Unearned repair revenue		3,800
Totals..	$358,600	$358,600

b.   _____ **Sid Whimsly, Capital** _____

Analysis component: _____

_____

_____

_____

_____

Exercise 5-14   Calculations:

a. **Current assets =**

[   ]

_____

_____

b. **Property, plant and equipment =**

[   ]

_____

_____

c. **Intangible assets =**

[   ]

_____

_____

d. **Long-term investments =**

[   ]

_____

_____

e. **Total assets =**

[   ]

_____

_____

f. **Current liabilities =**

[   ]

_____

_____

g. **Long-term liabilities =**

[   ]

_____

_____

h. **Total liabilities =**

[   ]

_____

_____

i. **Total liabilities and equity =**

[   ]

_____

_____

Balance Sheet			

Balance Sheet

a. _____
_____
_____
_____
_____

b. **Journalizing:**

GENERAL JOURNAL   Page____

Date	Account Titles and Explanation	PR	Debit	Credit

c. _____

Unadjusted Trial Balance

	Debit	Credit

b, d, g. Posting journal entries in (b), adjustments in (d), and closing entries in (g):

Cash

Bal. Dec. 31/11 2,000	

Accounts Receivable

Bal. Dec. 31/11 5,000	

Prepaid Rent

Bal. Dec. 31/11 3,000	

Office Equipment

Bal. Dec. 31/11 20,000	

Accum. Deprec., Office Equip.

	10,000 Bal. Dec. 31/11

Unearned Fees

	2,900 Bal. Dec. 31/11

Leda Svenson, Capital

	17,100 Bal. Dec. 31/11

Leda Svenson, Withdrawals

Bal. Dec. 31/11 -0-	

Tutoring Fees Earned

	-0- Bal. Dec. 31/11

Rent Expense

Bal. Dec. 31/11 -0-	

Depreciation Expense

Bal. Dec. 31/11 -0-	

Advertising Expense

Bal. Dec. 31/11 -0-	

Income Summary

d. Journalize adjustments:

GENERAL JOURNAL   Page____

Date	Account Titles and Explanation	PR	Debit	Credit

e. _____

Adjusted Trial Balance

	Debit	Credit

f. Financial statement preparation:

Income Statement

Statement of Changes in Equity

Balance Sheet

g. Journalize closing entries:

GENERAL JOURNAL   Page____

Date	Account Titles and Explanation	PR	Debit	Credit

h. _____

Post-Closing Trial Balance

	Debit	Credit

GENERAL JOURNAL   Page____

Date	Account Titles and Explanation	PR	Debit	Credit

*Exercise 5-19

1. Adjusting entries:

GENERAL JOURNAL   Page _____

Date	Account Titles and Explanation	PR	Debit	Credit

2. Subsequent entries without reversing:

GENERAL JOURNAL   Page _____

Date	Account Titles and Explanation	PR	Debit	Credit

GENERAL JOURNAL   Page _____

Date	Account Titles and Explanation	PR	Debit	Credit

3. Reversing entries and subsequent entries:

GENERAL JOURNAL   Page _____

Date	Account Titles and Explanation	PR	Debit	Credit

Nanimahoo Rentals

Work Sheet

For Year Ended March 31, 2011

Account Title	Unadjusted Trial Balance		Adjustments		Adjusted Trial Balance		Income Statement		Balance Sheet and Statement of Changes in Equity	
	Debit	Credit	Debit	Credit	Debit	Credit	Debit	Credit	Debit	Credit
Cash	17,000									
Rent receivable	60,000									
Office supplies	6,800									
Notes receivable, due 2014	143,000									
Furniture	46,000									
Building	625,000									
Land	110,000									
Patent	3,000									
Accounts payable		5,800								
Long-term note payable		375,000								
Joan Nanimahoo, capital		499,525								
Joan Nanimahoo, withdrawals	28,000									
Rent earned		406,200								
Office salaries expense	124,000									
Interest expense	20,625									
Advertising expense	28,000									
Janitorial expense	41,000									
Utilities expense	34,100									
Totals	1,286,525	1,286,525								

Trenton Consulting

Work Sheet

For Year Ended June 30, 2011

Account Title	Unadjusted Trial Balance		Adjustments		Adjusted Trial Balance		Income Statement		Balance Sheet and Statement of Changes in Equity	
	Debit	Credit	Debit	Credit	Debit	Credit	Debit	Credit	Debit	Credit
Cash	3,440									
Accounts receivable	2,990									
Prepaid rent	6,600									
Equipment	6,400									
Accounts payable		1,440								
Toni Trenton, capital		26,650								
Toni Trenton, withdrawals	800									
Consulting fees earned		30,200								
Wages expense	28,120									
Insurance expense	1,620									
Rent expense	8,320									
Totals	58,290	58,290								

Part 4

_____   _____
_____   **Toni Trenton, Capital**
_____   _____
_____

Analysis component:

_____
_____
_____
_____
_____
_____

Part 1

Challenger Construction

Work Sheet

For Year Ended September 30, 2011

Account Title	Unadjusted Trial Balance Debit	Unadjusted Trial Balance Credit	Adjustments Debit	Adjustments Credit	Adjusted Trial Balance Debit	Adjusted Trial Balance Credit	Income Statement Debit	Income Statement Credit	Balance Sheet and Statement of Changes in Equity Debit	Balance Sheet and Statement of Changes in Equity Credit
Cash	36,000									
Supplies	18,800									
Prepaid insurance	12,400									
Land not currently used	50,000									
Equipment	106,000									
Accum. deprec., equipment		40,500								
Copyright	6,000									
Accounts payable		9,600								
Interest payable										
Wages payable										
Long-term notes payable		50,000								
Chris Challenger, capital		55,320								
Chris Challenger, withdrawals	72,000									
Construction fees earned		280,000								
Deprec. Expense, equipment										
Wages expense	82,000									
Interest expense	3,000									
Insurance expense										
Rent expense	26,400									
Supplies expense										
Business taxes expense	10,000									
Repairs expense	5,020									
Utilities expense	7,800									
Totals	435,420	435,420								

Part 2
Adjusting entries:

GENERAL JOURNAL   Page____

Date	Account Titles and Explanation	PR	Debit	Credit
a.				
b.				
c.				
d.				
e.				
f.				

Part 2
Closing entries:

GENERAL JOURNAL   Page____

Date	Account Titles and Explanation	PR	Debit	Credit

Part 3

Income Statement

Statement of Changes in Equity

Balance Sheet

Analysis component:

a. _____

_____

_____

b. _____

_____

_____

Part 1   **GENERAL JOURNAL**   Page____

Date	Account Titles and Explanation	PR	Debit	Credit

Part 2

Post-Closing Trial Balance

Income Statement

Statement of Changes in Equity

Balance Sheet

Analysis component:

_____

_____

_____

_____

_____

_____

GENERAL JOURNAL

Page____

Date	Account Titles and Explanation	PR	Debit	Credit

Income Statement

Statement of Changes in Equity

Balance Sheet

Analysis component:

_____

_____

_____

_____

GENERAL JOURNAL

Date	Account Titles and Explanation	PR	Debit	Credit

Income Statement

Statement of Changes in Equity

Balance Sheet

Analysis component:

_____

_____

_____

_____

_____

_____

Part 1

Income Statement

Part 2

_____   **Noel Apex, Capital**
_____
_____
_____

Income Statement

Statement of Changes in Equity

Balance Sheet

Analysis component:

_____

_____

_____

_____

_____

_____

_____

Part 1

_____

_____   **Wyett North, Capital**
_____   _____

_____

_____

Part 2

_____

Balance Sheet

Analysis component:

_____

_____

_____

_____

_____

_____

_____

Part 1. Use either the balance column format or T-accounts; both are provided.

GENERAL LEDGER

Cash   ACCOUNT NO. 101

DATE	EXPLANATION	PR	DEBIT	CREDIT	BALANCE
2011					
June 30			40000		40000
		2		3200	36800
				2400	
				7200	
				3600	
			1300		
				3600	
				3500	
				2850	27250

Accounts Receivable   ACCOUNT NO. 106

DATE	EXPLANATION	PR	DEBIT	CREDIT	BALANCE
			3500		3500

Office Supplies   ACCOUNT NO. 124

DATE	EXPLANATION	PR	DEBIT	CREDIT	BALANCE
2011					
			2400		
				800	1600

Prepaid Insurance   ACCOUNT NO. 128

DATE	EXPLANATION	PR	DEBIT	CREDIT	BALANCE
			7200		
				400	6800

Furniture   ACCOUNT NO. 160

DATE	EXPLANATION	PR	DEBIT	CREDIT	BALANCE
			5000		5000

Accumulated Depreciation, Furniture   ACCOUNT NO. 161

DATE	EXPLANATION	PR	DEBIT	CREDIT	BALANCE
				400	400

Computer Equipment — ACCOUNT NO. 167

DATE	EXPLANATION	PR	DEBIT	CREDIT	BALANCE
			60000		60000

Accumulated Depreciation, Computer Equipment — ACCOUNT NO. 168

DATE	EXPLANATION	PR	DEBIT	CREDIT	BALANCE
				1650	1650

Accounts Payable — ACCOUNT NO. 201

DATE	EXPLANATION	PR	DEBIT	CREDIT	BALANCE
				700	700

Salaries Payable — ACCOUNT NO. 209

DATE	EXPLANATION	PR	DEBIT	CREDIT	BALANCE
				320	320

Sam Near, Capital — ACCOUNT NO. 301

DATE	EXPLANATION	PR	DEBIT	CREDIT	BALANCE
				105000	
			1070		
			2850		101080

Sam Near, Withdrawals — ACCOUNT NO. 302

DATE	EXPLANATION	PR	DEBIT	CREDIT	BALANCE
			2850		2850
				2850	0

Commissions Earned — ACCOUNT NO. 405

DATE	EXPLANATION	PR	DEBIT	CREDIT	BALANCE
				13600	
				3500	17100
			17100		0

Depreciation Expense, Furniture — ACCOUNT NO. 610

DATE	EXPLANATION	PR	DEBIT	CREDIT	BALANCE
			400		400
			400	400	0

Depreciation Expense, Computer Equipment — ACCOUNT NO. 612

DATE	EXPLANATION	PR	DEBIT	CREDIT	BALANCE
			1650		1650
				1650	0

Salaries Expense — ACCOUNT NO. 622

DATE	EXPLANATION	PR	DEBIT	CREDIT	BALANCE
			3600		
			3600		
			320		
				7320	0

Insurance Expense — ACCOUNT NO. 637

DATE	EXPLANATION	PR	DEBIT	CREDIT	BALANCE
			400		400
				0	

Rent Expense — ACCOUNT NO. 640

DATE	EXPLANATION	PR	DEBIT	CREDIT	BALANCE
2					
			400		400
				400	0

Office Supplies Expense — ACCOUNT NO. 650

DATE	EXPLANATION	PR	DEBIT	CREDIT	BALANCE
			800		800
				800	

Repairs Expense — ACCOUNT NO. 684

DATE	EXPLANATION	PR	DEBIT	CREDIT	BALANCE
			700		700
				700	0

Telephone Expense — ACCOUNT NO. 688

DATE	EXPLANATION	PR	DEBIT	CREDIT	BALANCE
			3500		3500
				3500	0

	Income Summary				ACCOUNT NO. 901
DATE	EXPLANATION	PR	DEBIT	CREDIT	BALANCE
				17 100	17 100
			18 170		1 070
				1 070	0

Part 1. Use either T-accounts or the balance column format; both are provided.

Cash	101		Accum. Deprec, Furniture	161

			Computer Equipment	167

			Accum. Deprec, Computer Equip	168

			Accounts Payable	201

Accounts Receivable	106		Salaries Payable	209

Office Supplies	124		Sam Near, Capital	301

Prepaid Insurance	128		Sam Near, Withdrawals	302

			Commissions Earned	405

Furniture	160			

Part 1. Use either T-accounts or the balance column format; both are provided.

| Deprec. Exp, Furniture   610 | Office Supplies Expense   650 |

| Deprec. Exp, Computer Equip.   612 | Repairs Expense   684 |

| Salaries Expense   622 | Telephone Expense   688 |

| | Income Summary   901 |

| Insurance Expense   637 | |

| Rent Expense   640 | |

Part 2. Transactions for June:

GENERAL JOURNAL   Page____

Date		Account Titles and Explanation	PR	Debit	Credit
June	1	Cash		40000	
		Furniture		5000	
		Computer Equipment		60000	
		Capital			105000
		To record companies Investment			
	2	Rent Expense		3200	
		Cash			3200
		Paid one month rent			
	3	Office Supplies		2400	
		Cash			2400
		Acquired office supplies			
	10	Prepard Insurance		7200	
		Cash			7200
		Paid one year Ins. in advance			
	14	Salary Expense		3600	
		Cash			3600
		Paid salary for 2 weeks			
	24	Cash		13600	
		Commissions earned			13600
		Collected commissions			
	28	Salary Expense		3600	
		Cash			3600
		Paid salary for 2 weeks			
	29	Telephone Expense		3500	
		Cash			3500
		Phone Bill Payment			
	30	Repair Expense		700	
		Accounts Payable			700
	30	Withdrawals		2850	
		cash			2850
		Owner withdrawal for cash			

Part 2. Transactions for June (cont'd.)

GENERAL JOURNAL   Page____

Date	Account Titles and Explanation	PR	Debit	Credit

Part 3. Adjusting entries:

GENERAL JOURNAL   Page____

Date	Account Titles and Explanation	PR	Debit	Credit
30	Insurance Expense		400	
	Prepaid Insurance			400
	600 × 2/3 = 400			
30	Office Supplies Expense		800	
	Office Supplies			800
	2400 - 1600 = 800			
	cost of consumed supplies			
30	Depreciation Expense, Fur		400	
	Accumulated Dep			400
30	Depreciation Expense, Equip		1650	
	Accumulated Depr.			1650
30	Salaries Expense		320	
	Salaries Payable			320
30	Accounts Receivable		3500	
	Commission Earned			3500
	To record accrued commission			

Part 4

Income Statement

Revenues:		
Commission Earned		17100
Operating Expenses		
Rent Expense	3200	
Salary Expe	3600	
Salary Expense	3600	
Telephone Expense	1500	
Repair Expense	700	
Salary Expense	320	
Office Supplies Expense	800	
Depreciation Exp Fur	400	
Insurance Expense	400	
Depreciation Expense Com Eq	1650	
		18170

Net Loss   1,070

Statement of Changes in Equity

		$
Sam cap June 1		
Add: Inv. by owner		105000
		105.000
Withd. by owner	2850	
Net Loss	1070	3920
Sam capital June 30		101,080

Balance Sheet

Part 5. Closing entries:

Reid

GENERAL JOURNAL   Page_____

Date		Account Titles and Explanation	PR	Debit	Credit
June	10	Commissions Earned		17100	
		Income Summary			17100
		Income Summary			
		Expenses			

Part 6

Post-Closing Trial Balance

	Debit	Credit

Part 1

GENERAL JOURNAL   Page____

Date	Account Titles and Explanation	PR	Debit	Credit
a.				
b.				
c.				
d.				
e.				
f.				

Part 2

GENERAL JOURNAL   Page____

Date	Account Titles and Explanation	PR	Debit	Credit

Part 3

GENERAL JOURNAL   Page____

Date	Account Titles and Explanation	PR	Debit	Credit

Daimler Tours

Work Sheet

For Year Ended July 31, 2011

Account Title	Unadjusted Trial Balance Debit	Unadjusted Trial Balance Credit	Adjustments Debit	Adjustments Credit	Adjusted Trial Balance Debit	Adjusted Trial Balance Credit	Income Statement Debit	Income Statement Credit	Balance Sheet and Statement of Changes in Equity Debit	Balance Sheet and Statement of Changes in Equity Credit
Cash	8,900									
Accounts receivable	21,250									
Notes receivable	14,000									
Prepaid insurance	10,500									
Furniture	6,750									
Accounts payable		6,925								
Unearned tour revenue		14,000								
Jan Rider, capital		60,975								
Jan Rider, withdrawals	-0-									
Tour revenue		15,500								
Wages expense	36,000									
Totals	97,400	97,400								

Parts 1, 2, and 3

Tucker Photographers

Work Sheet

For Year Ended December 31, 2011

Account Title	Unadjusted Trial Balance		Adjustments		Adjusted Trial Balance		Income Statement		Balance Sheet and Statement of Changes in Equity	
	Debit	Credit	Debit	Credit	Debit	Credit	Debit	Credit	Debit	Credit
Cash	28,000									
Accounts receivable	6,200									
Prepaid equipment rental	3,860									
Automobile	52,000									
Accum. deprec., automobile		-0-								
Accounts payable		1,920								
Unearned fees		5,740								
Jim Tucker, capital		78,800								
Jim Tucker, withdrawals	1,400									
Fees earned		8,400								
Deprec. Expense, automobile	-0-									
Equipment rental expense	3,400									
Totals	94,860	94,860								

© 2010 McGraw-Hill Ryerson Limited.

Part 4

_____   Jim Tucker, Capital
_____   _____|_____
_____ |
_____ |
                                                               |

Analysis component:

_____
_____
_____
_____
_____
_____
_____

Chapter 5   Problem 5-3B   Name _____

Part 1

Webster Demolition Company
Work Sheet
For Year Ended June 30, 2011

Account Title	Unadjusted Trial Balance Debit	Unadjusted Trial Balance Credit	Adjustments Debit	Adjustments Credit	Adjusted Trial Balance Debit	Adjusted Trial Balance Credit	Income Statement Debit	Income Statement Credit	Balance Sheet and Statement of Changes in Equity Debit	Balance Sheet and Statement of Changes in Equity Credit
Cash	4,500				4500					
Supplies	9,000			a)4050	4950					
Prepaid insurance	7,300			b)5750	1550					
Equipment	70,000				70000					
Accum. deprec., equipment		5,000		c)9000		14000				
Accounts payable		8,000		d)350		8350				
Interest payable				e)2100		2100				
Wages payable				f)1100		1100				
Long-term notes payable		45,000				45000				
Rusty Webster, capital		33,450				33450				33450
Rusty Webster, withdrawals	2,000				2000				2000	
Demolition fees earned		68,500				68500		68500		
Deprec. expense, equipment			c)9000		9000		9000			
Wages expense	25,700		f)1100		26800		26800			
Interest expense	1,100		e)2100		3200		3200			
Insurance expense			b)5750		5750		5750			
Rent expense	24,400				24400		24400			
Supplies expense			a)4050		4050		4050			
Business tax expense	4,200				4200		4200			
Repairs expense	3,350				3350		3350			
Utilities expense	8,400		d)350		8750		8750			10450
Totals	159,950	159,950			172500	172500	89500	21000	21000 (Loss)	

Part 2
Adjusting entries:

GENERAL JOURNAL   Page____

Date	Account Titles and Explanation	PR	Debit	Credit
a.				
b.				
c.				
d.				
e.				
f.				

Part 2
Closing entries:

Revenue → Income Sum.
Expenses → Income Sum.
Inc. Sum → owner's Capital
Drawings (withdrawal) → owner's Capital

GENERAL JOURNAL   Page____

Date		Account Titles and Explanation	PR	Debit	Credit	
		Demolition Fees Earned		6850		
		Income Summary			68500	+Income
		Income Summary		89500		
		Total Expense			89500	
		Capital		21000		
		Income Summary			21000	
		Capital		2000		
		Withdrawals			2000	

Revenues- Expenses

Part 3

Income Statement

Revenues:		
Demolition fees earned		$ 68500
Operating Expenses:		
Total	$ /	
	/	
		89500
		$ 21000

Statement of Changes in Equity

Investment by the owner		33450
Withdrawals by owner	2000	
Net loss	21000	
		10450

Balance Sheet

Assets			
Current Assets.			
Cash			
Accounts Receivable			
Office Supplies			
Prepaid Insurance			1600
Property, Plant and Equipment			
Equipment	70000		
Less: Accumulated dep Equipment	14000	56000	
			56000
			45000
Liabilities			2100
			1100
			6350
Equity			10450
			67000

Analysis component:

a. _____

_____

_____

b. _____

_____

_____

Revenue
Income
I

Part 1   GENERAL JOURNAL   Page____

Date		Account Titles and Explanation	PR	Debit	Credit
2011					
June	30	Sewing Fees Earned		124000	
		Income Summary			124000
		Income Summary		76120	
		Wages Expense			56800
		Insurance Expense			2200
		Rent Expense			4800
		Store Supplies			2600
		Utilities Expense			3720
		Capital		76120	
		Income Summary			76120
		Capital		32000	
		Withdrawals			32000

Part 2

Post-Closing Trial Balance		
June 30, 2011		
	Debit	Credit
Cash	26,900	
Store Supplies	8280	
Prepaid Insurance	4400	
Equipment	66000	
Acc. Depreciation Equipment		18000
Accounts Payable		42000
Wages Payable		8,400
Capital		39180
	105580	105580

Income Statement

Revenues		
Sewing Fees Earned		124 000
Operating Expenses		
Total	76 120	
		47 880

Statement of Changes in Equity

Investments by Owner		$23 300
Net Income		47 880
Withdrawals by owner	$32 000	
capital, December 31		39 180

Balance Sheet

Analysis component:

_____

_____

_____

_____

GENERAL JOURNAL   Page____

Date	Account Titles and Explanation	PR	Debit	Credit

Income Statement

Statement of Changes in Equity

Balance Sheet

Analysis component:

_____

_____

_____

_____

_____

GENERAL JOURNAL   Page____

Date	Account Titles and Explanation	PR	Debit	Credit

Income Statement

Statement of Changes in Equity

Balance Sheet

Analysis component:

_____

_____

_____

_____

_____

Part 1

Income Statement

Part 2

Grant Greenway, Capital

Income Statement

Statement of Changes in Equity

Balance Sheet

Analysis component:

_____

_____

_____

_____

_____

_____

Part 1

                                                        Jan Delta, Capital

Part 2

Balance Sheet

Part 1. Use either the balance column format or T-accounts; both are provided.

GENERAL LEDGER

Cash   ACCOUNT NO. 101

DATE	EXPLANATION	PR	DEBIT	CREDIT	BALANCE
			40000		
				3600	
				4600	
				10800	
				1800	
			17600		
				1800	
				600	34400

Accounts Receivable   ACCOUNT NO. 106

DATE	EXPLANATION	PR	DEBIT	CREDIT	BALANCE
			1900		1900

Office Supplies   ACCOUNT NO. 124

DATE	EXPLANATION	PR	DEBIT	CREDIT	BALANCE
			4600		
				3100	1500

Prepaid Insurance   ACCOUNT NO. 128

DATE	EXPLANATION	PR	DEBIT	CREDIT	BALANCE
			10800		
				600	10200

Land   ACCOUNT NO. 170

DATE	EXPLANATION	PR	DEBIT	CREDIT	BALANCE
			320000		320000

Buildings   ACCOUNT NO. 173

DATE	EXPLANATION	PR	DEBIT	CREDIT	BALANCE
			240000		240000

Accumulated Depreciation, Buildings   ACCOUNT NO. 174

DATE	EXPLANATION	PR	DEBIT	CREDIT	BALANCE
				2400	2400

Accounts Payable   ACCOUNT NO. 201

DATE	EXPLANATION	PR	DEBIT	CREDIT	BALANCE
				1700	1700

Salaries Payable   ACCOUNT NO. 209

DATE	EXPLANATION	PR	DEBIT	CREDIT	BALANCE
				360	360

Amy Young, Capital   ACCOUNT NO. 301

DATE	EXPLANATION	PR	DEBIT	CREDIT	BALANCE
				600000	
			3200	7140	
				7140	603940

Amy Young, Withdrawals   ACCOUNT NO. 302

DATE	EXPLANATION	PR	DEBIT	CREDIT	BALANCE
			3200		
				3200	0

Storage Fees Earned   ACCOUNT NO. 401

DATE	EXPLANATION	PR	DEBIT	CREDIT	BALANCE
			17600		
			1900		
				19500	0

Depreciation Expense, Buildings   ACCOUNT NO. 606

DATE	EXPLANATION	PR	DEBIT	CREDIT	BALANCE
			2400		
				2400	0

Salaries Expense   ACCOUNT NO. 622

DATE	EXPLANATION	PR	DEBIT	CREDIT	BALANCE
			1800		
			1800		
			360		
				3960	0

Insurance Expense   ACCOUNT NO. 637

DATE	EXPLANATION	PR	DEBIT	CREDIT	BALANCE
			600		
				600	0

Equipment Rental Expense   ACCOUNT NO. 640

DATE	EXPLANATION	PR	DEBIT	CREDIT	BALANCE
			3600		
				3600	0

Office Supplies Expense   ACCOUNT NO. 650

DATE	EXPLANATION	PR	DEBIT	CREDIT	BALANCE
			3100		
				3100	0

Repairs Expense   ACCOUNT NO. 684

DATE	EXPLANATION	PR	DEBIT	CREDIT	BALANCE
			1700		
				1700	

Telephone Expense   ACCOUNT NO. 688

DATE	EXPLANATION	PR	DEBIT	CREDIT	BALANCE
			600		
				600	0

Income Summary   ACCOUNT NO. 901

DATE	EXPLANATION	PR	DEBIT	CREDIT	BALANCE
				19500	
			12360		
			7140		0

Cash	101

Accounts Payable	201

Salaries Payable	209

Amy Young, Capital	301

6.5300

Accounts Receivable	106

Amy Young, Withdrawals	302

Storage Fees Earned	405

Office Supplies	124

Prepaid Insurance	128

Deprec. Exp., Buildings	606

Salaries Expense	622

Land	170

Insurance Expense	637

Buildings	173

Accum. Deprec., Buildings	174

Equipment Rental Expense	640

Office Supplies Expense 650		Telephone Expense 688

Repairs Expense 684		Income Summary 901

Part 2. Transactions for July:

GENERAL JOURNAL   Page____

Date		Account Titles and Explanation	PR	Debit	Credit
July	1	Cash		40000	
		Land		320000	
		Buildings		240000	
		Capital			600000
	2	Equipment Rental Ex		3600	
		Cash			3600
	5	Office Supplies		4600	
		Cash			4600
	10	Prepaid Insurance		10,800	
		Cash			10800
	14	Salaries Expense		1,800	
		Cash			1800
	24	Cash		17600	
		Storage Fees Earned			17600
	28	Salaries Expense		1800	
		Cash			1800

Part 2. Transactions for July (cont'd.)

GENERAL JOURNAL Page____

Date		Account Titles and Explanation	PR	Debit	Credit
	29	Telephone Expense		600	
		Cash			600
	30	Repair Expense		1700	
		Accounts Payable			1700
	31	Withdrawals		3200	
		Cash			3200

Part 3. Adjusting entries:

GENERAL JOURNAL   Page____

Date		Account Titles and Explanation	PR	Debit	Credit
2011					
July	31	Insurance Expense		600	
		Prepaid Insurance			600
		10.800/12 ✕ 2/3 =600			
	31	Office Supplies Expense		3100	
		Office Supplies			3100
	31	Depreciation Expense, Bul		2400	
		Accumulated Dep			2400
	31	Salary Expense		360	
		Salary Payable			360
	31	Accounts Receivable		1900	
		Storage Fees Earned			1900

Part 4

Income Statement

Revenues:		
Storage Fees Earned		19500
Operating Expenses		
	1800	
	1800	
	600	
12360	1700	
	600	
	3100	
	2400	
	360	
Total Operating Expense		7140

Statement of Changes in Equity

Capital, July 9		
Add: Investments by owner		600000
T. Net Income		7140
Total:		
Less: Withdrawals by owner	3200	
		603 940

Balance Sheet

Assets:			
Cash		34400	
Acc. Receivable		1900	
Office Supplies		1500	
Prepaid Insurance		10200	
Land		320000	
Building		240000	
Less: Acc. Depreciation	2600		
			605600
Liabilities			
Current Liabilities			
Accounts Payable		1700	
		360	
			606000
			605160

REID

Rev → Income
Expen → In?

Part 5. Closing entries:

GENERAL JOURNAL   Page____

Date		Account Titles and Explanation	PR	Debit	Credit
July	31	Storage Fees Earned		19500	
		Income Summary			19500
		Income Summary		12360	
		Expenses			12360
		Income Summary		7140	
		Capital			7140
		Capital		3200	
		Withdrawals			3200

Part 6

Post-Closing Trial Balance

	Debit	Credit
Cash	34400	
A. Receivable	1900	
	1500	
	10200	
	320000	
	240000	
		2400
		1700
		360
		603940

608400   608400

Part 1

GENERAL JOURNAL   Page____

Date	Account Titles and Explanation	PR	Debit	Credit

Part 2   GENERAL JOURNAL   Page____

Date	Account Titles and Explanation	PR	Debit	Credit

Part 3

GENERAL JOURNAL   Page____

Date	Account Titles and Explanation	PR	Debit	Credit

GENERAL JOURNAL   Page____

Date	Account Titles and Explanation	PR	Debit	Credit

GENERAL JOURNAL

Page____

Date	Account Titles and Explanation	PR	Debit	Credit

GENERAL LEDGER

Cash   ACCOUNT NO. 101

DATE	EXPLANATION	PR	DEBIT	CREDIT	BALANCE
2011 Dec. 31	Balance				89,090

Accounts Receivable   ACCOUNT NO. 106

DATE	EXPLANATION	PR	DEBIT	CREDIT	BALANCE
2011 Dec. 31	Balance				5,700

Computer Supplies   ACCOUNT NO. 126

DATE	EXPLANATION	PR	DEBIT	CREDIT	BALANCE
2011 Dec. 31	Balance				1,440

Prepaid Insurance   ACCOUNT NO. 128

DATE	EXPLANATION	PR	DEBIT	CREDIT	BALANCE
2011 Dec. 31	Balance				3,240

Prepaid Rent   ACCOUNT NO. 131

DATE	EXPLANATION	PR	DEBIT	CREDIT	BALANCE
2011 Dec. 31	Balance				2,250

Office Equipment   ACCOUNT NO. 163

DATE	EXPLANATION	PR	DEBIT	CREDIT	BALANCE
2011 Dec. 31	Balance				18,000

Accumulated Depreciation, Office Equipment   ACCOUNT NO. 164

DATE	EXPLANATION	PR	DEBIT	CREDIT	BALANCE
2011 Dec. 31	Balance				1,500

Computer Equipment   ACCOUNT NO. 167

DATE	EXPLANATION	PR	DEBIT	CREDIT	BALANCE
2011 Dec. 31	Balance				36,000

Accumulated Depreciation, Computer Equipment   ACCOUNT NO. 168

DATE	EXPLANATION	PR	DEBIT	CREDIT	BALANCE
2011 Dec. 31	Balance				2,250

Accounts Payable   ACCOUNT NO. 201

DATE	EXPLANATION	PR	DEBIT	CREDIT	BALANCE
2011 Dec. 31	Balance				2,310

Wages Payable   ACCOUNT NO. 210

DATE	EXPLANATION	PR	DEBIT	CREDIT	BALANCE
2011 Dec. 31	Balance				800

Unearned Computer Services Revenue   ACCOUNT NO. 236

DATE	EXPLANATION	PR	DEBIT	CREDIT	BALANCE
2011 Dec. 31	Balance				3,000

Mary Graham, Capital   ACCOUNT NO. 301

DATE	EXPLANATION	PR	DEBIT	CREDIT	BALANCE
2011 Dec. 31	Balance				144,000

Mary Graham, Withdrawals   ACCOUNT NO. 302

DATE	EXPLANATION	PR	DEBIT	CREDIT	BALANCE
2011 Dec. 31	Balance				14,400

Computer Services Revenue   ACCOUNT NO. 403

DATE	EXPLANATION	PR	DEBIT	CREDIT	BALANCE
2011 Dec. 31	Balance				52,200

Depreciation Expense, Office Equipment   ACCOUNT NO. 612

DATE	EXPLANATION	PR	DEBIT	CREDIT	BALANCE
2011 Dec. 31	Balance				1,500

Depreciation Expense, Computer Equipment   ACCOUNT NO. 613

DATE	EXPLANATION	PR	DEBIT	CREDIT	BALANCE
2011 Dec. 31	Balance				2,250

Wages Expense   ACCOUNT NO. 623

DATE	EXPLANATION	PR	DEBIT	CREDIT	BALANCE
2011 Dec. 31	Balance				6,200

Insurance Expense   ACCOUNT NO. 637

DATE	EXPLANATION	PR	DEBIT	CREDIT	BALANCE
2011 Dec. 31	Balance				1,080

Rent Expense   ACCOUNT NO. 640

DATE	EXPLANATION	PR	DEBIT	CREDIT	BALANCE
2011 Dec. 31	Balance				6,750

Computer Supplies Expense   ACCOUNT NO. 652

DATE	EXPLANATION	PR	DEBIT	CREDIT	BALANCE
2011 Dec. 31	Balance				5,430

Advertising Expense   ACCOUNT NO. 655

DATE	EXPLANATION	PR	DEBIT	CREDIT	BALANCE
2011 Dec. 31	Balance				5,820

Mileage Expense   ACCOUNT NO. 676

DATE	EXPLANATION	PR	DEBIT	CREDIT	BALANCE
2011 Dec. 31	Balance				2,800

Repairs Expense, Computer   ACCOUNT NO. 684

DATE	EXPLANATION	PR	DEBIT	CREDIT	BALANCE
2011 Dec. 31	Balance				2,610

Charitable Donations Expense   ACCOUNT NO. 699

DATE	EXPLANATION	PR	DEBIT	CREDIT	BALANCE
2011 Dec. 31	Balance				1,500

Income Summary   ACCOUNT NO. 901

DATE	EXPLANATION	PR	DEBIT	CREDIT	BALANCE
2011 Dec. 31	Balance				

Part 2

ECHO SYSTEMS
Post-Closing Trial Balance
December 31, 2011

	Debit	Credit

	a.	b.	c.	d.	e.
Net sales					
Cost of goods sold					
Gross profit from sales					
Operating expenses					
Net income (loss)					

Quick Study 6-2

a. _____

b. _____

c. _____

d. _____

e. _____

Quick Study 6-3

a. _____

_____

b. _____

_____

Quick Study 6-4

a. _____

_____

b. _____

_____

_____

Quick Study 6-5

GENERAL JOURNAL   Page____

Date	Account Titles and Explanation	PR	Debit	Credit

GENERAL JOURNAL   Page____

Date	Account Titles and Explanation	PR	Debit	Credit

Quick Study 6-6

GENERAL JOURNAL   Page____

Date	Account Titles and Explanation	PR	Debit	Credit

Quick Study 6-7

GENERAL JOURNAL   Page____

Date	Account Titles and Explanation	PR	Debit	Credit

GENERAL JOURNAL   Page____

Date		Account Titles and Explanation	PR	Debit	Credit

Quick Study 6-8

GENERAL JOURNAL   Page____

Date		Account Titles and Explanation	PR	Debit	Credit

Name _____

GENERAL JOURNAL

Page____

Date	Account Titles and Explanation	PR	Debit	Credit

Quick Study 6-10

GENERAL JOURNAL

Page____

Date	Account Titles and Explanation	PR	Debit	Credit

GENERAL JOURNAL   Page____

Date		Account Titles and Explanation	PR	Debit	Credit

Quick Study 6-11

	a.	b.	c.	d.

Calculations:

_____

_____

_____

_____

_____

_____

_____

_____

Quick Study 6-12

GENERAL JOURNAL   Page____

Date		Account Titles and Explanation	PR	Debit	Credit

Calculations:

_____

_____

_____

a. Classified Multi-Step:

Income Statement

b. Single-Step:

Income Statement

_____
_____
_____
_____
_____
_____
_____
_____

Quick Study 6-15

GENERAL JOURNAL   Page____

Date	Account Titles and Explanation	PR	Debit	Credit

Name _____

a.

GENERAL JOURNAL

Page____

Date	Account Titles and Explanation	PR	Debit	Credit

b.

GENERAL JOURNAL

Page____

Date	Account Titles and Explanation	PR	Debit	Credit

c.   GENERAL JOURNAL   Page____

Date	Account Titles and Explanation	PR	Debit	Credit

*Quick Study 6-17

a.   GENERAL JOURNAL   Page____

Date	Account Titles and Explanation	PR	Debit	Credit

b.   **GENERAL JOURNAL**   Page____

Date	Account Titles and Explanation	PR	Debit	Credit

c.   **GENERAL JOURNAL**   Page____

Date	Account Titles and Explanation	PR	Debit	Credit

*Quick Study 6-19

GENERAL JOURNAL   Page____

Date	Account Titles and Explanation	PR	Debit	Credit

	a.	b.	c.	d.

Calculations:

_____

_____

_____

_____

_____

*Quick Study 6-21

GENERAL JOURNAL   Page____

Date	Account Titles and Explanation	PR	Debit	Credit

*Quick Study 6-22

GENERAL JOURNAL   Page____

Date	Account Titles and Explanation	PR	Debit	Credit

GENERAL JOURNAL   Page____

Date	Account Titles and Explanation	PR	Debit	Credit

*Quick Study 6-24

GENERAL JOURNAL   Page____

Date	Account Titles and Explanation	PR	Debit	Credit

Exercise 6-1

	a.	b.	c.	d.	e.
Sales	240,000	140,000	75,000		
Cost of goods sold			42,000	268,000	46,000
Gross profit from sales	114,000				39,000
Operating expenses	95,000	82,000		146,000	
Net income (loss)		(28,000)	(8,000)	48,000	(14,000)

GENERAL JOURNAL

Date	Account Titles and Explanation	PR	Debit	Credit

GENERAL JOURNAL   Page____

Date	Account Titles and Explanation	PR	Debit	Credit

GENERAL JOURNAL   Page____

Date	Account Titles and Explanation	PR	Debit	Credit

GENERAL JOURNAL

Page____

Date	Account Titles and Explanation	PR	Debit	Credit

GENERAL JOURNAL   Page____

Date	Account Titles and Explanation	PR	Debit	Credit

GENERAL JOURNAL   Page____

Date	Account Titles and Explanation	PR	Debit	Credit
a.	Purchaser entries (Sundown):			
b.	Seller entries (Raintree):			

Analysis component:

_____

_____

_____

_____

_____

_____

_____

_____

_____

a.   **Entries journalized by Wilson Purchasing:**

GENERAL JOURNAL   Page____

Date	Account Titles and Explanation	PR	Debit	Credit

b.   **Entries journalized by Hostel Sales:**

GENERAL JOURNAL   Page____

Date	Account Titles and Explanation	PR	Debit	Credit

GENERAL JOURNAL
Page____

Date	Account Titles and Explanation	PR	Debit	Credit

Analysis component:

_____
_____
_____
_____
_____
_____
_____
_____
_____
_____
_____
_____

Exercise 6-8

1.	6.
2.	7.
3.	8.
4.	9.
5.	10.

Merchandise Inventory	Cost of Goods Sold

Analysis component:

_____
_____
_____
_____
_____
_____
_____
_____
_____
_____
_____
_____

Exercise 6-10

a. _____
b. _____
c. _____
d. _____

Analysis component:

_____
_____
_____
_____
_____
_____
_____
_____

	Company A		Company B	
	2011	2010	2011	2010
Sales	256,000	160,000		50,000
Sales discounts	2,560		1,100	500
Sales returns and allowances		16,000	5,500	
Net sales		142,400		47,000
Cost of goods sold	153,600		55,000	
Gross profit from sales	48,640		48,400	22,000
Selling expenses	17,920	16,000	24,200	
Administrative expenses	25,600		29,700	11,000
Total operating expenses		40,000		
Net income (loss)		14,400		2,000
Gross profit ratio				

Calculations:

_____
_____
_____
_____
_____
_____

Analysis component:

_____
_____
_____
_____
_____
_____

Exercise 6-12

	a.	b.	c.
Purchases			
Purchases discounts			
Purchase returns and allowances			
Transportation-in			
Cost of goods purchased			
Beginning inventory			
Cost of goods purchased			
Ending inventory			
Cost of goods sold			

	Company A		Company B	
	2011	2010	2011	2010
Sales	120,000	180,000	90,000	
Cost of goods sold:				
Merch. inventory (beginning)	18,700	22,300	9,875	9,000
Total cost of merchandise purchases	72,000			26,100
Merch. Inventory (ending)		(18,700)	(8,920)	(9,875)
Cost of goods sold	74,300	108,000		
Gross profit from sales			39,545	19,775
Operating expenses	36,000	54,000	27,000	
Net income (loss)	9,700	18,000		6,275
Gross profit ratio				

Analysis component:

_____

_____

_____

_____

Exercise 6-14	a.	b.	c.
Invoice cost of merch. purchases	45,000	20,000	15,250
Purchase discounts	2,000		325
Purchase returns and allowances	1,500	750	550
Cost of transportation-in		1,750	2,000
Merchandise inventory (beginning)	3,500		4,500
Net cost of merchandise purchases	44,700	19,750	
Merchandise inventory (ending)	2,200	3,750	
Cost of goods sold		20,800	17,065

Exercise 6-15

a.

_____

Income Statement

b.   GENERAL JOURNAL   Page____

Date	Account Titles and Explanation	PR	Debit	Credit

c: _____   **Peter Delta, Capital**
_____
_____
_____

Analysis component:
_____
_____
_____
_____
_____
_____
_____
_____
_____

Part a

Perdu Sales

Work Sheet

For Year Ended December 31, 2011

Account Title	Unadjusted Trial Balance Debit	Unadjusted Trial Balance Credit	Adjustments Debit	Adjustments Credit	Adjusted Trial Balance Debit	Adjusted Trial Balance Credit	Income Statement Debit	Income Statement Credit	Balance Sheet and Statement of Changes in Equity Debit	Balance Sheet and Statement of Changes in Equity Credit
Cash	26,000									
Merchandise inventory	2,000									
Prepaid selling expenses	8,000									
Store equipment	40,000									
Accum. deprec., store equip.		9,000								
Accounts payable		14,840								
Salaries payable		0								
Eldon Perdu, capital		45,600								
Eldon Perdu, withdrawals	3,600									
Sales		858,000								
Sales returns and allowances	33,000									
Sales discounts	8,000									
Cost of goods sold	424,840									
Sales salaries expense	94,000									
Utilities expense, store	28,000									
Other selling expenses	70,000									
Other administrative expenses	190,000									
Totals	927,440	927,440								

Income Statement

Part c   **GENERAL JOURNAL**   Page____

Date	Account Titles and Explanation	PR	Debit	Credit

GENERAL JOURNAL   Page____

Date		Account Titles and Explanation	PR	Debit	Credit

Analysis component:

_____

_____

_____

_____

_____

_____

_____

_____

Exercise 6-17

a. _____

b. _____

Income Statement

GENERAL JOURNAL

Page____

Date	Account Titles and Explanation	PR	Debit	Credit

GENERAL JOURNAL

Date	Account Titles and Explanation	PR	Debit	Credit

GENERAL JOURNAL

Page____

Date	Account Titles and Explanation	PR	Debit	Credit

GENERAL JOURNAL

Date	Account Titles and Explanation	PR	Debit	Credit

GENERAL JOURNAL   Page____

Date	Account Titles and Explanation	PR	Debit	Credit

*Exercise 6-22

GENERAL JOURNAL   Page____

Date	Account Titles and Explanation	PR	Debit	Credit

GENERAL JOURNAL   Page____

Date	Account Titles and Explanation	PR	Debit	Credit

*Exercise 6-23

GENERAL JOURNAL   Page____

Date	Account Titles and Explanation	PR	Debit	Credit

GENERAL JOURNAL

Page____

Date	Account Titles and Explanation	PR	Debit	Credit

a.

b.

c.

d. _____

Analysis component:

Dewer's Stop'n Shop

Work Sheet

For Year Ended December 31, 2011

Account Title	Unadjusted Trial Balance		Adjustments		Income Statement		Balance Sheet and Statement of Changes in Equity	
	Debit	Credit	Debit	Credit	Debit	Credit	Debit	Credit
Cash	7,400							
Accounts receivable	3,600							
Merchandise inventory	2,400							
Store supplies	1,200							
Accounts payable		280						
Salaries payable								
Mi Dewer, capital		11,570						
Mi Dewer, withdrawals	750							
Sales		12,000						
Sales returns and allowances	290							
Purchases	6,400							
Purchase discounts		250						
Transportation-in	160							
Salaries expense	1,400							
Rent expense	500							
Store supplies expense								
Totals	24,100	24,100						

a.

b.

c.

d.

Income Statement

a. _____

b. _____

c. _____

Income Statement

d.   GENERAL JOURNAL   Page____

Date	Account Titles and Explanation	PR	Debit	Credit

e.

_____   John Yu, Capital
_____   _____
_____ |
_____ |
_____ |
_____ |

GENERAL JOURNAL   Page____

Date		Account Titles and Explanation	PR	Debit	Credit

*Exercise 6-30

GENERAL JOURNAL   Page____

Date		Account Titles and Explanation	PR	Debit	Credit

Date		Account Titles and Explanation	PR	Debit	Credit

GENERAL JOURNAL

Page____

Date	Account Titles and Explanation	PR	Debit	Credit

Part 2

_____
_____
_____
_____
_____

Problem 6-2A

GENERAL JOURNAL

Page____

Date	Account Titles and Explanation	PR	Debit	Credit

GENERAL JOURNAL

Date	Account Titles and Explanation	PR	Debit	Credit

GENERAL JOURNAL   Page____

Date		Account Titles and Explanation	PR	Debit	Credit

Analysis component:

_____

_____

_____

_____

_____

_____

_____

_____

_____

_____

_____

Name _____

GENERAL JOURNAL   Page____

Date	Account Titles and Explanation	PR	Debit	Credit

GENERAL JOURNAL

Page____

Date	Account Titles and Explanation	PR	Debit	Credit

Part 1

Jumbo's
Work Sheet
For Year Ended December 31, 2011

Account Title	Unadjusted Trial Balance Debit	Unadjusted Trial Balance Credit	Adjustments Debit	Adjustments Credit	Adjusted Trial Balance Debit	Adjusted Trial Balance Credit	Income Statement Debit	Income Statement Credit	Balance Sheet and Statement of Changes in Equity Debit	Balance Sheet and Statement of Changes in Equity Credit
Cash	10,275									
Accounts receivable	22,665									
Merchandise inventory	54,365									
Store supplies	2,415									
Office supplies	775									
Prepaid insurance	3,255									
Equipment	74,490									
Accum. depreciation, equip.		13,655								
Accounts payable		8,000								
Salaries payable										
Sally Fowler, capital		166,015								
Sally Fowler, withdrawals	15,000									
Interest revenue		310								
Sales		502,140								
Sales returns and allowances	5,070									
Cost of goods sold	381,160									
Salaries expenses	91,550									
Rent expense	29,100									
Supplies expense										
Depreciation exp., equipment										
Insurance expense										
Totals	690,120	690,120								

Income Statement

Analysis component:

_____

_____

_____

_____

_____

_____

_____

Income Statement

Income Statement

GENERAL JOURNAL

Date	Account Titles and Explanation	PR	Debit	Credit

Part 1 – Classified, multiple-step

Income Statement

Part 2 – Single-step

Income Statement		

Analysis component:

_____

_____

_____

_____

_____

_____

_____

GENERAL JOURNAL   Page____

Date	Account Titles and Explanation	PR	Debit	Credit

Part 1 – Classified, multiple-step

Income Statement

Part 2 – Multiple-step

Income Statement

Part 3 – Single-step

Income Statement

Analysis component:

GENERAL JOURNAL

Date	Account Titles and Explanation	PR	Debit	Credit

GENERAL JOURNAL   Page____

Date	Account Titles and Explanation	PR	Debit	Credit

GENERAL JOURNAL   Page____

Date	Account Titles and Explanation	PR	Debit	Credit

1. _____

2. _____

3. _____

4. _____

Income Statement

5.

Income Statement

GENERAL JOURNAL

Page____

Date		Account Titles and Explanation	PR	Debit	Credit

Part 1

Woodstock Store
Work Sheet
For Year Ended December 31, 2011

Account Title	Unadjusted Trial Balance Debit	Unadjusted Trial Balance Credit	Adjustments Debit	Adjustments Credit	Income Statement Debit	Income Statement Credit	Balance Sheet and Statement of Changes in Equity Debit	Balance Sheet and Statement of Changes in Equity Credit
Cash	7,305							
Merchandise inventory	47,000							
Store supplies	1,715							
Office supplies	645							
Prepaid insurance	3,960							
Store equipment	57,615							
Accum. deprec., store equip.		8,750						
Office equipment	14,400							
Accum. deprec., office equip.		9,000						
Accounts payable		4,000						
Zen Woodstock, capital		89,080						
Zen Woodstock, withdrawals	31,500							
Rental revenue		680						
Sales		478,850						
Sales returns and allowances	2,915							
Sales discounts	5,190							
Purchases	331,315							
Purchase returns and allowances		1,845						
Purchase discounts		4,725						
Transportation-in	2,810							
Sales salaries expenses	34,710							
Rent expense, selling space	24,000							
Advertising expense	1,220							
Store supplies expense								
Deprec. exp., store equipment								
Office salaries expense	27 630							
Rent expense, office space	3,000							
Office supplies expense								
Insurance expense								
Deprec. exp., office equipment								
Totals	596,930	596,930						

Part 2   GENERAL JOURNAL   Page____

Date	Account Titles and Explanation	PR	Debit	Credit

GENERAL LEDGER

Merchandise Inventory   ACCOUNT NO. 119

DATE	EXPLANATION	PR	DEBIT	CREDIT	BALANCE

Income Statement

*Problem 6-16A

GENERAL JOURNAL   Page___

Date	Account Titles and Explanation	PR	Debit	Credit

GENERAL JOURNAL

Page____

Date	Account Titles and Explanation	PR	Debit	Credit

GENERAL JOURNAL

Date	Account Titles and Explanation	PR	Debit	Credit

GENERAL JOURNAL

Page____

Date	Account Titles and Explanation	PR	Debit	Credit

Part 1   **GENERAL JOURNAL**   Page____

Date	Account Titles and Explanation	PR	Debit	Credit

GENERAL JOURNAL

Page____

Date		Account Titles and Explanation	PR	Debit	Credit

Part 2

_____

_____

_____

_____

_____

Problem 6-2B

GENERAL JOURNAL

Page__

Date		Account Titles and Explanation	PR	Debit	Credit

GENERAL JOURNAL   Page____

Date	Account Titles and Explanation	PR	Debit	Credit

GENERAL JOURNAL   Page____

Date	Account Titles and Explanation	PR	Debit	Credit

Analysis component:

_____
_____
_____
_____
_____
_____
_____
_____
_____
_____
_____
_____
_____
_____
_____

GENERAL JOURNAL

Page____

Date	Account Titles and Explanation	PR	Debit	Credit

GENERAL JOURNAL   Page____

Date	Account Titles and Explanation	PR	Debit	Credit

Analysis component:

_____

_____

_____

_____

_____

_____

Part 1

Journey's End Company
Work Sheet
For Year Ended October 31, 2011

Account Title	Unadjusted Trial Balance		Adjustments		Adjusted Trial Balance		Income Statement		Balance Sheet and Statement of Changes in Equity	
	Debit	Credit	Debit	Credit	Debit	Credit	Debit	Credit	Debit	Credit
Cash	12,800									
Merchandise inventory	46,000									
Store supplies	18,900									
Prepaid insurance	9,500									
Store equipment	167,600									
Accum. deprec., store equip.		60,000								
Accounts payable		32,000								
Dallas End, capital		160,800								
Dallas End, withdrawals	12,000									
Sales		396,000								
Sales discounts	4,000									
Sales returns and allowances	8,000									
Cost of goods sold	149,600									
Deprec. expense, store equip.										
Salaries expense	124,000									
Interest expense	800									
Insurance expense										
Rent expense	56,000									
Store supplies expense										
Advertising expense	39,600									
Totals	648,800	648,800								

_____

Income Statement

Analysis component:

_____

_____

_____

_____

_____

_____

_____

Name _____

1. Classified, multiple-step

Income Statement

2. Single-step

Income Statement

GENERAL JOURNAL

Date	Account Titles and Explanation	PR	Debit	Credit

Part 1 – Classified, multiple-step

Income Statement

Part 2 – Single-step

Income Statement

Analysis component:

_____

_____

_____

_____

GENERAL JOURNAL

Date	Account Titles and Explanation	PR	Debit	Credit

Part 1 – Classified, multiple-step

Income Statement

Part 2 – Multiple-step

Income Statement

Part 3 – Single-step

Income Statement

*Problem 6-10B

GENERAL JOURNAL   Page____

Date		Account Titles and Explanation	PR	Debit	Credit

GENERAL JOURNAL

Page____

Date	Account Titles and Explanation	PR	Debit	Credit

GENERAL JOURNAL   Page____

Date	Account Titles and Explanation	PR	Debit	Credit

GENERAL JOURNAL

Page____

Date	Account Titles and Explanation	PR	Debit	Credit

1. _____
_____
_____
_____
_____
_____
_____
_____

2. _____
_____
_____
_____
_____
_____
_____
_____
_____

3. _____
_____
_____
_____
_____
_____
_____
_____
_____
_____
_____

4. Multiple-step

Income Statement

5. Single-step

Income Statement

GENERAL JOURNAL

Date	Account Titles and Explanation	PR	Debit	Credit

Part 1

The Online Store
Work Sheet
For Year Ended March 31, 2011

Account Title	Unadjusted Trial Balance		Adjustments		Income Statement		Balance Sheet and Statement of Changes in Equity	
	Debit	Credit	Debit	Credit	Debit	Credit	Debit	Credit
Cash	7,000							
Merchandise inventory	48,000							
Supplies	600							
Prepaid rent	7,000							
Store equipment	60,000							
Accum. deprec., store equip.		14,000						
Office equipment	23,000							
Accum. deprec., office equip.		6,500						
Accounts payable		16,000						
Lucy Baker, capital		134,600						
Lucy Baker, withdrawals	34,000							
Sales		499,000						
Sales returns and allowances	11,500							
Sales discounts	6,000							
Purchases	346,000							
Purchase returns and allowances		2,850						
Purchase discounts		7,150						
Transportation-in	16,000							
Salaries expenses	60,000							
Rent expense	45,500							
Advertising expense	7,000							
Supplies expense	8,500							
Deprec. exp., store equipment	0							
Deprec. exp., office equipment	0							
Totals	680,100	680,100						

Part 2   GENERAL JOURNAL   Page____

Date	Account Titles and Explanation	PR	Debit	Credit

Part 3

GENERAL LEDGER

Merchandise Inventory   ACCOUNT NO. 110

DATE	EXPLANATION	PR	DEBIT	CREDIT	BALANCE

Income Statement

GENERAL JOURNAL

Page____

Date	Account Titles and Explanation	PR	Debit	Credit

GENERAL JOURNAL   Page____

Date	Account Titles and Explanation	PR	Debit	Credit

*Problem 6-17B

GENERAL JOURNAL   Page____

Date	Account Titles and Explanation	PR	Debit	Credit

GENERAL JOURNAL

Date	Account Titles and Explanation	PR	Debit	Credit

GENERAL JOURNAL   Page____

Date	Account Titles and Explanation	PR	Debit	Credit

Part 1   Echo Systems (cont'd.)

GENERAL JOURNAL   Page____

Date	Account Titles and Explanation	PR	Debit	Credit

GENERAL JOURNAL   Page____

Date	Account Titles and Explanation	PR	Debit	Credit

GENERAL JOURNAL

Page____

Date	Account Titles and Explanation	PR	Debit	Credit

GENERAL LEDGER

Cash   ACCOUNT NO. 101

DATE	EXPLANATION	PR	DEBIT	CREDIT	BALANCE
2011 Dec. 31	Balance				89,090

Part 2   Echo Systems (cont'd.)

Accounts Receivable – Alamo Engineering   ACCOUNT NO. 106.1

DATE	EXPLANATION	PR	DEBIT	CREDIT	BALANCE
2011 Dec. 31	Balance				-0-

Accounts Receivable – Buckman Services   ACCOUNT NO. 106.2

DATE	EXPLANATION	PR	DEBIT	CREDIT	BALANCE
2011 Dec. 31	Balance				-0-

Accounts Receivable – Capital Leasing   ACCOUNT NO. 106.3

DATE	EXPLANATION	PR	DEBIT	CREDIT	BALANCE
2011 Dec. 31	Balance				-0-

Accounts Receivable – Decker Co.   ACCOUNT NO. 106.4

DATE	EXPLANATION	PR	DEBIT	CREDIT	BALANCE
2011 Dec. 31	Balance				2,700

Accounts Receivable – Elite Corporation   ACCOUNT NO. 106.5

DATE	EXPLANATION	PR	DEBIT	CREDIT	BALANCE
2011 Dec. 31	Balance				-0-

Accounts Receivable – Fostek Co.   ACCOUNT NO. 106.6

DATE	EXPLANATION	PR	DEBIT	CREDIT	BALANCE
2011 Dec. 31	Balance				3,000

Accounts Receivable – Grandview Co.   ACCOUNT NO. 106.7

DATE	EXPLANATION	PR	DEBIT	CREDIT	BALANCE
2011 Dec. 31	Balance				-0-

Accounts Receivable – Hacienda, Inc.   ACCOUNT NO. 106.8

DATE	EXPLANATION	PR	DEBIT	CREDIT	BALANCE
2011 Dec. 31	Balance				-0-

Accounts Receivable – Images, Inc.   ACCOUNT NO. 106.9

DATE	EXPLANATION	PR	DEBIT	CREDIT	BALANCE
2011 Dec. 31	Balance				-0-

Part 2   Echo Systems (cont'd.)

Merchandise Inventory   ACCOUNT NO. 119

DATE	EXPLANATION	PR	DEBIT	CREDIT	BALANCE

Computer Supplies   ACCOUNT NO. 126

DATE	EXPLANATION	PR	DEBIT	CREDIT	BALANCE
2011 Dec. 31	Balance				1,440

Prepaid Insurance   ACCOUNT NO. 128

DATE	EXPLANATION	PR	DEBIT	CREDIT	BALANCE
2011 Dec. 31	Balance				3,240

Prepaid Rent   ACCOUNT NO. 131

DATE	EXPLANATION	PR	DEBIT	CREDIT	BALANCE
2011 Dec. 31	Balance				2,250

Office Equipment   ACCOUNT NO. 163

DATE	EXPLANATION	PR	DEBIT	CREDIT	BALANCE
2011 Dec. 31	Balance				18,000

Accumulated Depreciation, Office Equipment — ACCOUNT NO. 164

DATE	EXPLANATION	PR	DEBIT	CREDIT	BALANCE
2011 Dec. 31	Balance				1,500

Computer Equipment — ACCOUNT NO. 167

DATE	EXPLANATION	PR	DEBIT	CREDIT	BALANCE
2011 Dec. 31	Balance				36,000

Accumulated Depreciation, Computer Equipment — ACCOUNT NO. 168

DATE	EXPLANATION	PR	DEBIT	CREDIT	BALANCE
2011 Dec. 31	Balance				2,250

Accounts Payable — ACCOUNT NO. 201

DATE	EXPLANATION	PR	DEBIT	CREDIT	BALANCE
2011 Dec. 31	Balance				2,310

Wages Payable — ACCOUNT NO. 210

DATE	EXPLANATION	PR	DEBIT	CREDIT	BALANCE
2011 Dec. 31	Balance				800

Part 2   Echo Systems (cont'd.)

Unearned Computer Services Revenue   ACCOUNT NO. 236

DATE	EXPLANATION	PR	DEBIT	CREDIT	BALANCE
2011 Dec. 31	Balance				3,000

Mary Graham, Capital   ACCOUNT NO. 301

DATE	EXPLANATION	PR	DEBIT	CREDIT	BALANCE
2011 Dec. 31	Balance				145,860

Mary Graham, Withdrawals   ACCOUNT NO. 302

DATE	EXPLANATION	PR	DEBIT	CREDIT	BALANCE

Computer Services Revenue   ACCOUNT NO. 403

DATE	EXPLANATION	PR	DEBIT	CREDIT	BALANCE

Sales   ACCOUNT NO. 413

DATE	EXPLANATION	PR	DEBIT	CREDIT	BALANCE

Sales Discounts   ACCOUNT NO. 414

DATE	EXPLANATION	PR	DEBIT	CREDIT	BALANCE

Sales Returns and Allowances   ACCOUNT NO. 415

DATE	EXPLANATION	PR	DEBIT	CREDIT	BALANCE

Cost of Goods Sold   ACCOUNT NO. 502

DATE	EXPLANATION	PR	DEBIT	CREDIT	BALANCE

Depreciation Expense, Office Equipment   ACCOUNT NO. 612

DATE	EXPLANATION	PR	DEBIT	CREDIT	BALANCE

Depreciation Expense, Computer Equipment   ACCOUNT NO. 613

DATE	EXPLANATION	PR	DEBIT	CREDIT	BALANCE

Wages Expense   ACCOUNT NO. 623

DATE	EXPLANATION	PR	DEBIT	CREDIT	BALANCE

Part 2   Echo Systems (cont'd.)

Insurance Expense   ACCOUNT NO. 637

DATE	EXPLANATION	PR	DEBIT	CREDIT	BALANCE

Rent Expense   ACCOUNT NO. 640

DATE	EXPLANATION	PR	DEBIT	CREDIT	BALANCE

Computer Supplies Expense   ACCOUNT NO. 652

DATE	EXPLANATION	P.R.	DEBIT	CREDIT	BALANCE

Advertising Expense   ACCOUNT NO. 655

DATE	EXPLANATION	PR	DEBIT	CREDIT	BALANCE

Mileage Expense   ACCOUNT NO. 676

DATE	EXPLANATION	PR	DEBIT	CREDIT	BALANCE

Repairs Expense, Computer   ACCOUNT NO. 684

DATE	EXPLANATION	PR	DEBIT	CREDIT	BALANCE

Charitable Donations Expense   ACCOUNT NO. 699

DATE	EXPLANATION	PR	DEBIT	CREDIT	BALANCE

ECHO SYSTEMS
Partial Work Sheet
For Three Months Ended March 31, 2012

Acct. No.	Account Title	Unadjusted Trial Balance Dr.	Cr.	Adjustments Dr.	Cr.	Adjusted Trial Balance Dr.	Cr.
101	Cash						
106.1	Alamo Engineering Co.						
106.2	Buckman Services						
106.3	Capital Leasing						
106.4	Decker Co.						
106.5	Elite Corporation						
106.6	Fostek Co.						
106.7	Grandview Co.						
106.8	Hacienda Inc.						
106.9	Images Inc.						
119	Merchandise inventory						
126	Computer supplies						
128	Prepaid insurance						
131	Prepaid rent						
163	Office equipment						
164	Accum. deprec., office equipment						
167	Computer equipment						
168	Accum. deprec., computer equip.						
201	Accounts payable						
210	Wages payable						
236	Unearned computer services rev.						
301	Mary Graham, capital						
302	Mary Graham, withdrawals						
403	Computer services revenue						
413	Sales						
414	Sales discounts						
415	Sales returns and allowances						
502	Cost of goods sold						
612	Deprec. exp., office equipment						
613	Deprec. exp., computer equip.						
623	Wages expense						
637	Insurance expense						
640	Rent expense						
652	Computer supplies expense						
655	Advertising expense						
676	Mileage expense						
684	Repairs expense, computer						
699	Charitable donations expense						
	Totals						

Part 4   Echo Systems (cont'd.)

ECHO SYSTEMS
Income Statement
For Three Months Ended March 31, 2012

Part 5

ECHO SYSTEMS
Statement of Changes in Equity
For Three Months Ended March 31, 2012

ECHO SYSTEMS
Balance Sheet
March 31, 2012

Part 1   **Echo Systems**
Journal Entries

GENERAL JOURNAL   Page _____

Date	Account Titles and Explanation	PR	Debit	Credit

Date	Account Titles and Explanation	PR	Debit	Credit

Date	Account Titles and Explanation	PR	Debit	Credit

Date	Account Titles and Explanation	PR	Debit	Credit

GENERAL LEDGER

Cash   ACCOUNT NO. 101

DATE	EXPLANATION	PR	DEBIT	CREDIT	BALANCE
2011 Dec. 31	Balance				89,090

Part 2   Echo Systems (cont'd.)

Accounts Receivable – Alamo Engineering   ACCOUNT NO. 106.1

DATE	EXPLANATION	PR	DEBIT	CREDIT	BALANCE
2011 Dec. 31	Balance				-0-

Accounts Receivable – Buckman Services   ACCOUNT NO. 106.2

DATE	EXPLANATION	PR	DEBIT	CREDIT	BALANCE
2011 Dec. 31	Balance				-0-

Accounts Receivable – Capital Leasing   ACCOUNT NO. 106.3

DATE	EXPLANATION	PR	DEBIT	CREDIT	BALANCE
2011 Dec. 31	Balance				-0-

Accounts Receivable – Decker Co.   ACCOUNT NO. 106.4

DATE	EXPLANATION	PR	DEBIT	CREDIT	BALANCE
2011 Dec. 31	Balance				2,700

Accounts Receivable – Elite Corporation   ACCOUNT NO. 106.5

DATE	EXPLANATION	PR	DEBIT	CREDIT	BALANCE
2011 Dec. 31	Balance				-0-

Accounts Receivable – Fostek Co.   ACCOUNT NO. 106.6

DATE	EXPLANATION	PR	DEBIT	CREDIT	BALANCE
2011 Dec. 31	Balance				3,000

Accounts Receivable – Grandview Co.   ACCOUNT NO. 106.7

DATE	EXPLANATION	PR	DEBIT	CREDIT	BALANCE
2011 Dec. 31	Balance				-0-

Accounts Receivable – Hacienda, Inc.   ACCOUNT NO. 106.8

DATE	EXPLANATION	PR	DEBIT	CREDIT	BALANCE
2011 Dec. 31	Balance				-0-

Accounts Receivable – Images, Inc.   ACCOUNT NO. 106.9

DATE	EXPLANATION	PR	DEBIT	CREDIT	BALANCE
2011 Dec. 31	Balance				-0-

Merchandise Inventory   ACCOUNT NO. 119

DATE	EXPLANATION	PR	DEBIT	CREDIT	BALANCE

Computer Supplies   ACCOUNT NO. 126

DATE	EXPLANATION	PR	DEBIT	CREDIT	BALANCE
2011 Dec. 31	Balance				1,440

Prepaid Insurance   ACCOUNT NO. 128

DATE	EXPLANATION	PR	DEBIT	CREDIT	BALANCE
2011 Dec. 31	Balance				3,240

Prepaid Rent   ACCOUNT NO. 131

DATE	EXPLANATION	PR	DEBIT	CREDIT	BALANCE
2011 Dec. 31	Balance				2,250

Office Equipment   ACCOUNT NO. 163

DATE	EXPLANATION	PR	DEBIT	CREDIT	BALANCE
2011 Dec. 31	Balance				18,000

Accumulated Depreciation, Office Equipment   ACCOUNT NO. 164

DATE	EXPLANATION	PR	DEBIT	CREDIT	BALANCE
2011 Dec. 31	Balance				1,500

Computer Equipment   ACCOUNT NO. 167

DATE	EXPLANATION	PR	DEBIT	CREDIT	BALANCE
2011 Dec. 31	Balance				36,000

Accumulated Depreciation, Computer Equipment   ACCOUNT NO. 168

DATE	EXPLANATION	PR	DEBIT	CREDIT	BALANCE
2011 Dec. 31	Balance				2,250

Accounts Payable   ACCOUNT NO. 201

DATE	EXPLANATION	PR	DEBIT	CREDIT	BALANCE
2011 Dec. 31	Balance				2,310

Wages Payable   ACCOUNT NO. 210

DATE	EXPLANATION	PR	DEBIT	CREDIT	BALANCE
2011 Dec. 31	Balance				800

Unearned Computer Services Revenue   ACCOUNT NO. 236

DATE	EXPLANATION	PR	DEBIT	CREDIT	BALANCE
2011 Dec. 31	Balance				3,000

Mary Graham, Capital   ACCOUNT NO. 301

DATE	EXPLANATION	PR	DEBIT	CREDIT	BALANCE
2011 Dec. 31	Balance				145,860

Mary Graham, Withdrawals   ACCOUNT NO. 302

DATE	EXPLANATION	PR	DEBIT	CREDIT	BALANCE

Computer Services Revenue   ACCOUNT NO. 403

DATE	EXPLANATION	PR	DEBIT	CREDIT	BALANCE

Sales   ACCOUNT NO. 413

DATE	EXPLANATION	PR	DEBIT	CREDIT	BALANCE

Sales Discounts   ACCOUNT NO. 414

DATE	EXPLANATION	PR	DEBIT	CREDIT	BALANCE

Sales Returns and Allowances   ACCOUNT NO. 415

DATE	EXPLANATION	PR	DEBIT	CREDIT	BALANCE

Purchases   ACCOUNT NO. 505

DATE	EXPLANATION	PR	DEBIT	CREDIT	BALANCE

Purchase Returns and Allowances   ACCOUNT NO. 506

DATE	EXPLANATION	PR	DEBIT	CREDIT	BALANCE

Purchase Discounts   ACCOUNT NO.507

DATE	EXPLANATION	PR	DEBIT	CREDIT	BALANCE

Transportation-In   ACCOUNT NO. 508

DATE	EXPLANATION	PR	DEBIT	CREDIT	BALANCE

Depreciation Expense, Office Equipment   ACCOUNT NO. 612

DATE	EXPLANATION	PR	DEBIT	CREDIT	BALANCE

Depreciation Expense, Computer Equipment   ACCOUNT NO. 613

DATE	EXPLANATION	PR	DEBIT	CREDIT	BALANCE

Wages Expense   ACCOUNT NO. 623

DATE	EXPLANATION	PR	DEBIT	CREDIT	BALANCE

Insurance Expense   ACCOUNT NO. 637

DATE	EXPLANATION	PR	DEBIT	CREDIT	BALANCE

Rent Expense   ACCOUNT NO. 640

DATE	EXPLANATION	PR	DEBIT	CREDIT	BALANCE

Computer Supplies Expense   ACCOUNT NO. 652

DATE	EXPLANATION	P.R.	DEBIT	CREDIT	BALANCE

Advertising Expense   ACCOUNT NO. 655

DATE	EXPLANATION	PR	DEBIT	CREDIT	BALANCE

Mileage Expense   ACCOUNT NO. 676

DATE	EXPLANATION	PR	DEBIT	CREDIT	BALANCE

Repairs Expense, Computer   ACCOUNT NO. 684

DATE	EXPLANATION	PR	DEBIT	CREDIT	BALANCE

Charitable Donations Expense   ACCOUNT NO. 699

DATE	EXPLANATION	PR	DEBIT	CREDIT	BALANCE

Part 3   Echo Systems (concl'd.)

ECHO SYSTEMS
Partial Work Sheet
March 31, 2012

Acct. No.	Account Title	Unadjusted Trial Balance		Adjustments		Adjusted Trial Balance	
		Debit	Credit	Debit	Credit	Debit	Credit
101	Cash						
106.1	Alamo Engineering Co.						
106.2	Buckman Services						
106.3	Capital Leasing						
106.4	Decker Co.						
106.5	Elite Corporation						
106.6	Fostek Co.						
106.7	Grandview Co.						
106.8	Hacienda Inc.						
106.9	Images Inc.						
119	Merchandise inventory						
126	Computer supplies						
128	Prepaid insurance						
131	Prepaid rent						
163	Office equipment						
164	Accum. deprec., office equipment						
167	Computer equipment						
168	Accum. deprec., computer equip.						
201	Accounts payable						
210	Wages payable						
236	Unearned computer services rev.						
301	Mary Graham, capital						
302	Mary Graham, withdrawals						
403	Computer services revenue						
413	Sales						
414	Sales discounts						
415	Sales returns and allowances						
505	Purchases						
506	Purchase returns and allowances						
507	Purchase discounts						
508	Transportation-in						
612	Deprec. exp., office equipment						
613	Deprec. exp., computer equip.						
623	Wages expense						
637	Insurance expense						
640	Rent expense						
652	Computer supplies expense						
655	Advertising expense						
676	Mileage expense						
684	Repairs expense, computer						
699	Charitable donations expense						
	Totals						

Parts 4, 5, and 6: Use the forms provided on pages 445 to 446 inclusive.

1. _____
_____
_____

2. _____
_____
_____

Quick Study 7-2

_____
_____
_____
_____
_____

Quick Study 7-3

_____
_____
_____
_____
_____

Quick Study 7-4

_____
_____
_____
_____
_____

Quick Study 7-5

_____
_____
_____
_____
_____
_____
_____
_____
_____
_____
_____
_____

a. FIFO Perpetual

Date	Purchases	Sales (at cost)	Inventory Balance

b. Moving Weighted Average Perpetual

Date	Purchases	Sales (at cost)	Inventory Balance

Date	Purchases	Sales (at cost)	Inventory Balance

Quick Study 7-8

Date	Purchases/ Transportation-In/ (Purchase Returns/Discounts) Units	Cost Per Unit	Total $	Cost of Goods Sold/ (Returns to Inventory) Units	Cost Per Unit	Total $	Balance in Inventory Units	Avg Cost Per Unit	Total $
Jan. 1		BFWD					10	$15.00	$150.00
3				6					
7	25	$18.50	$462.50						
8			50.00						
17			(46.25)						
18				14					

Calculations:

_____

_____

_____

_____

_____

_____

_____

Quick Study 7-9

a. _____

b. _____

c. _____

Parts a and b

Inventory Items	Units on Hand	Per Unit		Total Cost	Total NRV	LCNRV applied to:	
		Cost	NRV			a. Inventory as a Group	b. Each Product
Aprons	9	$6.00	$5.50				
Bottles	12	3.50	4.25				
Candles	25	8.00	7.00				

Part c

GENERAL JOURNAL　　　　　　Page____

Date	Account Titles and Explanation	PR	Debit	Credit

Quick Study 7-11

a. _____

b. _____

c. _____

d. _____

e. _____

f. _____

Quick Study 7-12

_____
_____
_____
_____
_____
_____
_____
_____
_____
_____
_____
_____
_____
_____
_____
_____
_____

a. _____
_____
_____
_____
_____
_____
_____
_____
_____
_____
_____

b. _____

Quick Study 7-14

_____
_____
_____
_____
_____
_____
_____
_____
_____
_____
_____
_____

Quick Study 7-15

_____
_____
_____
_____
_____
_____
_____
_____
_____
_____
_____
_____
_____
_____
_____
_____
_____

_____
_____
_____
_____
_____
_____
_____
_____
_____
_____
_____
_____
_____
_____

*Quick Study 7-17

_____
_____
_____
_____
_____
_____
_____
_____
_____

*Quick Study 7-18

a. Days' sales in inventory: _____

_____
_____
_____
_____
_____
_____
_____

b. Merchandise turnover: _____

_____
_____
_____
_____
_____
_____
_____

a. FIFO Perpetual

Date	Purchases	Sales (at cost)	Inventory Balance

Gross profit calculation under FIFO:

b. Moving weighted Average Perpetual

Date	Purchases	Sales (at cost)	Inventory Balance

Gross Profit Calculation under Moving Weighted Average:

_____
_____
_____
_____
_____
_____

Exercise 7-2

Specific Identification

Date	Purchases	Sales (at cost)	Inventory Balance

Gross Profit Calculation Under Specific Identification:

_____
_____
_____
_____
_____

1. _____

_____

_____

_____

_____

_____

_____

_____

2. _____

_____

_____

_____

_____

3(a). FIFO perpetual

Date	Purchases	Sales (at cost)	Inventory Balance

3(b). Moving weighted-average perpetual

Date	Purchases	Sales (at cost)	Inventory Balance

Exercise 7-4

Specific Identification

Date	Purchases	Sales (at cost)	Inventory Balance

	Trout, Inc.		
	Income Statements		
	For the Year Ended December 31, 2011		
	FIFO	Moving Weighted Average	Specific Identification

1. _____

2. _____
   _____

Exercise 7-6

Date	Purchases/ Transportation-In/ (Purchase Returns/Discounts)			Cost of Goods Sold/ (Returns to Inventory)			Balance in Inventory		
	Units	Cost Per Unit	Total $	Units	Cost Per Unit	Total $	Units	Avg Cost Per Unit	Total $
Mar. 1		BFWD					50	$95.00	$4,750.00
2	25	$97.00							
3				12					
4				(2)					
7				48					
17	15	92.00							
28				25					

Calculations:
_____
_____
_____
_____
_____

Analysis component:
_____
_____
_____
_____

Parts a and b

Inventory Items	Units on Hand	Per Unit Cost	Per Unit NRV	Total Cost	Total NRV	LCNRV applied to: a. Inventory as a Group	LCNRV applied to: b. Each Product
BB	22	$100	$108				
FM	15	156	144				
MB	36	190	182				
SL	40	72	87				

Part c   **GENERAL JOURNAL**   Page____

Date	Account Titles and Explanation	PR	Debit	Credit

1. _____

_____

_____

2.

For years ended December 31, 2011, 2012, and 2013 Income statement information should have been reported as:	Income statement information actually reported for years ended December 31,		
	2011	2012	2013
Sales			
Cost of goods sold:			
Beginning inventory			
+ Purchases			
- Ending inventory			
= Cost of goods sold			
Gross profit			

_____
_____
_____
_____
_____
_____
_____
_____
_____
_____
_____
_____
_____
_____

Exercise 7-10

	At Cost	At Retail

Exercise 7-11

a. Estimated cost of physical inventory:

_____
_____
_____

b. Shrinkage at cost and at retail:

	At Cost	At Retail

	Ending Inventory	Cost of Goods Sold

a. FIFO periodic: _____

_____

_____

_____

_____

b. Weighted-average cost periodic: _____

_____

_____

_____

_____

_____

Which method provides the lower net income and why?

_____

_____

_____

*Exercise 7-13

	Ending Inventory	Cost of Goods Sold

a. FIFO periodic: _____

_____

_____

_____

_____

b. Weighted-average cost periodic: _____

_____

_____

_____

_____

Which method provides the lower net income and why?

_____

_____

_____

_____
_____
_____
_____
_____
_____
_____
_____
_____
_____
_____
_____
_____
_____
_____

*Exercise 7-15

Merchandise turnover (2012): _____
_____
_____
_____

Merchandise turnover (2011): _____
_____
_____
_____

Days' sales in inventory (2012): _____
_____
_____
_____

Days' sales in inventory (2011): _____
_____
_____
_____

Comment on Russo's efficiency in using its assets to support increasing sales from 2011 to 2012.

_____
_____
_____
_____

1b. FIFO Perpetual

Date	Purchases			Sales (at cost)			Inventory Balance		
	Units	Cost	Total						
1/1	500 ×	90	45000				500	90	45000
10/2	250	84	21000				500	90	45000
							250	84	21000
15/3				330	90	29700	170	90	15300
							250	84	21000
21/8	130	100	13000				170	90	15300
							250	84	21000
							130	100	13000
10/9				170	90	15300	185	84	15540
				65	84	5460	130	100	13000
		79000			50460				28540

1b. Moving Weighted-Average Perpetual

Date	Purchases			Cost of Goods Sold			Inventory Balance		
1/1	500	90	45000				500	90	45000
10/2	250	84	21000				750	88	66000
15/3				330	88	(29040)	420	88	3996000
21/8	130	100	13000				550	90.84	4996000
10/9				235	90.84	(21347u)	315	90.84	28612-60

2. Specific Identification

Date	Purchases			Cost of Goods Sold			Inventory Balance		
1/1	500	90	45000				500	90	45000
10/2	250	84	21000				500	90	45000
							250	84	21000
15/3				170	90	15300	330	90	29700
				160	84	13440	90	84	7560
21/8	130	100	13000				330	90	29700
							90	84	7560
							130	100	13000
10/9				165	90	14850	165	90	14850
				20	84	1680	70	84	5560
				50	100	5000	80	100	8000

3.

GENERAL JOURNAL   Page____

	Date	Account Titles and Explanation	PR	Debit	Credit
a.					
b.					

GENERAL JOURNAL   Page____

Date	Account Titles and Explanation	PR	Debit	Credit
c.				

a. FIFO basis:

_____
_____
_____
_____
_____
_____
_____

b. Weighted Average basis:

_____
_____
_____
_____
_____
_____
_____

Problem 7-3A

Calculation of cost of goods available for sale and units available for sale:

_____
_____
_____
_____
_____
_____
_____
_____
_____

Calculation of units in ending inventory:

_____
_____
_____
_____
_____
_____

1a. FIFO Perpetual

Date	Purchases	Cost of Goods Sold	Inventory Balance

1b. Moving Weighted-Average Perpetual

Date	Purchases	Cost of Goods Sold	Inventory Balance

2.

	FIFO	Moving Weighted Average
Sales...............................		
Cost of goods sold		
Gross profit		

Analysis component:

_____

_____

_____

_____

_____

*Problem 7-4A

a. FIFO basis:

b. Weighted Average basis:

Fresh Express Company
Income Statement Comparing FIFO and Moving Weighted Average Cost
For Year Ended December 31, 2011

	FIFO	Moving Weighted Average
Sales		
Cost of goods sold		
Gross profit		
Operating expenses		
Net income		

Supporting calculations:

_____
_____
_____
_____
_____
_____
_____
_____
_____
_____
_____
_____
_____

1a. FIFO Perpetual

Date	Purchases	Cost of Goods Sold	Inventory Balance

1b. Moving Weighted-Average Perpetual

Date	Purchases	Cost of Goods Sold	Inventory Balance

Analysis component:

_____
_____
_____
_____
_____
_____
_____

*Problem 7-6A

Fresh Express Company		
Income Statement Comparing FIFO and Weighted Average Periodic		
For Year Ended December 31, 2011		
	FIFO	**Weighted Average**
Sales		
Cost of goods sold		
Gross profit		
Operating expenses		
Net income		

Supporting calculations:

_____
_____
_____
_____
_____
_____
_____
_____
_____
_____
_____
_____
_____
_____
_____

Analysis component:

_____
_____
_____
_____
_____
_____
_____

Name _____

Part 1

a. Cost of Goods Sold:	2011	2012	2013
Reported...................................	_____	_____	_____
Adjustments: 12/31/2011 error	_____	_____	_____
12/31/2012 error	_____	_____	_____
Corrected................................	_____	_____	_____

b. Net Income:	2011	2012	2013
Reported...................................	_____	_____	_____
Adjustments: 12/31/2011 error	_____	_____	_____
12/31/2012 error	_____	_____	_____
Corrected................................	_____	_____	_____

c. Total Current Assets:	2011	2012	2013
Reported...................................	_____	_____	_____
Adjustments: 12/31/2011 error	_____	_____	_____
12/31/2012 error	_____	_____	_____
Corrected................................	_____	_____	_____

d. Equity:	2011	2012	2013
Reported...................................	_____	_____	_____
Adjustments: 12/31/2011 error	_____	_____	_____
12/31/2012 error	_____	_____	_____
Corrected................................	_____	_____	_____

Analysis component:

_____
_____
_____
_____
_____
_____
_____
_____
_____
_____
_____
_____
_____
_____
_____
_____

	2011	2012	2013
Corrected Ending Inventory			
Corrected Cost of Goods Sold			
Corrected Net Income			

Problem 7-9A

		Per Unit				LCNRV applied to:	
Inventory Items	Units on Hand	Cost	NRV	Total Cost	Total NRV	a. Major Group	b. Separately to Each Product
Audio equip:							
Receivers	335	$180	$ 196				
CD players	250	222	200				
Cassette decks	316	172	190				
Turntables	194	104	82				
Video:							
Televisions	470	300	250				
VCRs	281	186	168				
Video cameras	202	620	644				
Car Audio:							
Cassette radios	175	140	168				
CD radios	160	194	210				

2a.   GENERAL JOURNAL   Page____

Date		Account Titles and Explanation	PR	Debit	Credit

2b.   GENERAL JOURNAL   Page____

Date		Account Titles and Explanation	PR	Debit	Credit

Problem 7-10A

Part 1

Earthly Goods
Estimated Inventory
December 31, 2011

	At Cost	*At Retail*

Part 2

Earthly Goods
Inventory Shortage
December 31, 2011

	At Cost	*At Retail*

Part 1

	At Cost	At Retail

Part 2

*Problem 7-14A

Part 1

Part 2
a. FIFO basis:

_____
_____
_____
_____
_____
_____
_____

b. Weighted Average basis:

_____
_____
_____
_____
_____
_____
_____

1a. FIFO Perpetual

Date	Purchases	Sales (at cost)	Inventory Balance

1b. Moving Weighted-Average Perpetual

Date	Purchases	Sales (at cost)	Inventory Balance

2. Specific Identification

Date	Purchases	Cost of Goods Sold	Inventory Balance

3.   GENERAL JOURNAL   Page____

Date	Account Titles and Explanation	PR	Debit	Credit
a.				
b.				
c.				

a. FIFO basis:

_____

_____

_____

_____

_____

_____

_____

b. Weighted Average basis:

_____

_____

_____

_____

_____

_____

1a. FIFO Perpetual

Date	Purchases	Cost of Goods Sold	Inventory Balance

1b. Moving Weighted-Average Perpetual

Date	Purchases	Cost of Goods Sold	Inventory Balance

2.

	FIFO	Moving Weighted Average
Sales......................................		
Cost of goods sold		
Gross profit		

Analysis component: _____

_____

_____

_____

_____

_____

*Problem 7-4B

a. FIFO basis:

_____

_____

_____

_____

_____

_____

c. Weighted Average basis:

_____

_____

_____

_____

_____

_____

_____

The Blizzard Company
Income Statement Comparing FIFO and Moving Weighted Average Cost
For Year Ended December 31, 2011

	FIFO	Moving Weighted Average
Sales		
Cost of goods sold		
Gross profit		
Operating expenses		
Net income		

Supporting calculations:

_____

_____

_____

_____

_____

_____

_____

_____

_____

_____

_____

_____

_____

_____

_____

_____

1a. FIFO Perpetual

Date	Purchases	Cost of Goods Sold	Inventory Balance

1b. Moving Weighted-Average Perpetual

Date	Purchases	Cost of Goods Sold	Inventory Balance

Analysis component:

_____
_____
_____
_____
_____
_____
_____
_____
_____

The Blizzard Company
Income Statement Comparing FIFO and Weighted Average Periodic
For Year Ended December 31, 2011

	FIFO	Weighted Average
Sales		
Cost of goods sold		
Gross profit		
Operating expenses		
Net income		

Supporting calculations:

_____
_____
_____
_____
_____
_____
_____
_____
_____
_____

a. FIFO Periodic

_____
_____
_____
_____
_____
_____
_____
_____

b. Weighted Average Periodic

_____
_____
_____
_____
_____
_____
_____
_____

Name _____

Part 1

a. Cost of Goods Sold:	*2011*	*2012*	*2013*
Reported...............................	_____	_____	_____
Adjustments: 12/31/2011 error	_____	_____	_____
12/31/2012 error	_____	_____	_____
Corrected..	_____	_____	_____

b. Net Income:	*2011*	*2012*	*2013*
Reported.......................................	_____	_____	_____
Adjustments: 12/31/2011 error	_____	_____	_____
12/31/2012 error	_____	_____	_____
Corrected..	_____	_____	_____

c. Total Current Assets:	*2011*	*2012*	*2013*
Reported.......................................	_____	_____	_____
Adjustments: 12/31/2011 error	_____	_____	_____
12/31/2012 error	_____	_____	_____
Corrected..	_____	_____	_____

d. Equity:	*2011*	*2012*	*2013*
Reported.......................................	_____	_____	_____
Adjustments: 12/31/2011 error	_____	_____	_____
12/31/2012 error	_____	_____	_____
Corrected..	_____	_____	_____

Analysis component:

_____
_____
_____
_____
_____
_____
_____
_____
_____
_____
_____
_____
_____
_____
_____

Chapter 7   Problem 7-8B   *Name* _____

Part 1

	Incorrect Income Statement Information For Years Ended December 31				Corrected Income Statement Information For Years Ended December 31			
	2011	%	2012	%	2011	%	2012	%
Sales								
Cost of goods sold ...								
Gross profit								

Part 2

_____

_____

_____

_____

Problem 7-9B

Inventory Items	Units on Hand	Per Unit		Total Cost	Total NRV	LCNRV applied to:	
		Cost	NRV			a. Major Category	b. Separately to Each Product
Office furniture:							
Desks	436	$261	$305				
Credenzas	295	227	256				
Chairs	587	49	43				
Bookshelves	321	93	82				
Filing cabinets:							
Two-drawer	214	81	70				
Four-drawer	398	135	122				
Lateral	175	104	118				
Office Equip.:							
Fax machines	430	168	200				
Copiers	545	317	288				
Typewriters	352	125	117				

2a. GENERAL JOURNAL   Page____

Date	Account Titles and Explanation	PR	Debit	Credit

2b. GENERAL JOURNAL   Page____

Date	Account Titles and Explanation	PR	Debit	Credit

Problem 7-10B

Part 1

THE WILKE CO.
Estimated Inventory
December 31, 2011

	At Cost	At Retail

Part 2

THE WILKE CO.
Inventory Shortage
December 31, 2011

	At Cost	At Retail

Part 1

	At Cost	At Retail

*Problem 7-14B   Part 1

Part 2
a. FIFO basis:

c. Weighted Average basis:

1. _____   3. _____
2. _____   4. _____

Quick Study 8-2

1. _____   5. _____
2. _____   6. _____
3. _____   7. _____
4. _____   8. _____

Quick Study 8-3

a. _____   e. _____
b. _____   f. _____
c. _____   g. _____
d. _____

Quick Study 8-4

GENERAL JOURNAL   Page____

Date	Account Titles and Explanation	PR	Debit	Credit

Quick Study 8-5

1. _____   5. _____
2. _____   6. _____
3. _____   7. _____
4. _____

Quick Study 8-6

1. _____   5. _____
2. _____   6. _____
3. _____   7. _____
4. _____

Quick Study 8-7

				Sales Journal	Page
Date	Account Debited	Invoice Number	PR	Accounts Receivable Dr. Sales Cr.	Cost of Goods Sold Dr. Merchandise Inventory Cr.

Quick Study 8-8

			Cash Receipts Journal						Page
Date	Account Credited	PR	Explanation	Cash Dr.	Sales Disc. Dr.	Accts. Rec. Cr.	Sales Cr.	Other Accts. Cr.	COGS Dr. Merch. Inv. Cr.

Quick Study 8-9

				Purchases Journal				Page
Date	Account Credited	Date of Invoice	Terms	PR	Accounts Payable Cr.	Merch. Inventory Dr.	Office Supplies Dr.	Other Accounts Dr.

Cash Disbursements Journal								Page
Date	Ch. No.	Payee	Account Debited	PR	Cash Cr.	Merch. Inventory Cr.	Other Accounts Dr.	Accounts Payable Dr.

Exercise 8-1

Sales Journal						Page
Date	Account Debited	Invoice Number	PR	Accounts Receivable Dr. Sales Cr.	Cost of Goods Sold Dr. Merchandise Inventory Cr.	

*Exercise 8-2

Sales Journal				Page
Date	Account Debited	Invoice No.	PR	Accounts Receivable Dr. Sales Cr.

Exercise 8-3

Cash Receipts Journal									Page
Date	Account Credited	PR	Explanation	Cash Dr.	Sales Disc. Dr.	Accts. Rec. Cr.	Sales Cr.	Other Accts. Cr.	COGS Dr. Merch. Inv. Cr.

| Cash Receipts Journal | | | | | | | | Page |
Date	Account Credited	PR	Explanation	Cash Dr.	Sales Disc. Dr.	Accts. Rec. Cr.	Sales Cr.	Other Accts. Cr.

Exercise 8-5

| Purchases Journal | | | | | | | | Page |
Date	Account Credited	Date of Invoice	Terms	PR	Accounts Payable Cr.	Merch. Inventory Dr.	Office Supplies Dr.	Other Accounts Dr.

*Exercise 8-6

| Purchases Journal | | | | | | | | Page |
Date	Account Credited	Date of Invoice	Terms	PR	Accts. Payable Cr.	Purchases Dr.	Office Supplies Dr.	Other Accts. Dr.

Exercise 8-7

| Cash Disbursements Journal | | | | | | | | Page |
Date	Ch. No.	Payee	Account Debited	PR	Cash Cr.	Merch. Inventory Cr.	Other Accounts Dr.	Accounts Payable Dr.

Cash Disbursements Journal								Page
Date	Ch. No.	Payee	Account Debited	PR	Cash Cr.	Purch. Disc. Cr.	Other Accounts Dr.	Accts. Payable Dr.

Exercise 8-9

Part 1 – Wilson Purchasing

Purchases Journal								Page
Date	Account Credited	Date of Invoice	Terms	PR	Accounts Payable Cr.	Merch. Inventory Dr.	Office Supplies Dr.	Other Accounts Dr.

Cash Disbursements Journal								Page
Date	Ch. No.	Payee	Account Debited	PR	Cash Cr.	Merch. Inventory Cr.	Other Accounts Dr.	Accounts Payable Dr.

GENERAL JOURNAL   Page____

Date	Account Titles and Explanation	PR	Debit	Credit

Part 2 – Hostel Sales

				Sales Journal		Page
Date	Account Debited	Invoice Number	PR	Accounts Receivable Dr. Sales Cr.		Cost of Goods Sold Dr. Merchandise Inventory Cr.

			Cash Receipts Journal						Page
Date	Account Credited	PR	Explanation	Cash Dr.	Sales Disc. Dr.	Accts. Rec. Cr.	Sales Cr.	Other Accts. Cr.	COGS Dr. Merch. Inv. Cr.

GENERAL JOURNAL   Page____

Date	Account Titles and Explanation	PR	Debit	Credit

*Exercise 8-10

Part 1 – Wilson Purchasing

					Purchases Journal			Page
Date	Account Credited	Date of Invoice	Terms	PR	Accts. Payable Cr.	Purchases Dr.	Office Supplies Dr.	Other Accts. Dr.

Cash Disbursements Journal								Page
Date	Ch. No.	Payee	Account Debited	PR	Cash Cr.	Purch. Disc. Cr.	Other Accounts Dr.	Accts. Payable Dr.

GENERAL JOURNAL   Page____

Date	Account Titles and Explanation	PR	Debit	Credit

Part 2 – Hostel Sales

Sales Journal				Page
Date	Account Debited	Invoice No.	PR	Accounts Receivable Dr. Sales Cr.

Cash Receipts Journal								Page
Date	Account Credited	PR	Explanation	Cash Dr.	Sales Disc. Dr.	Accts. Rec. Cr.	Sales Cr.	Other Accts. Cr.

GENERAL JOURNAL   Page____

Date	Account Titles and Explanation	PR	Debit	Credit

_____
_____
_____
_____
_____
_____
_____
_____
_____
_____
_____
_____

Exercise 8-12

a. _____

b. _____

c. _____

d. _____

e. _____

Exercise 8-13

Part 1   ACCOUNTS RECEIVABLE SUBLEDGER

Sanders Farrell	Don Holland	Brad Smithers

Part 2   GENERAL LEDGER

Accounts Receivable	Sales	Sales Returns and Allowances

Part 3

Schedule of Accounts Receivable

*Exercise 8-14

Parts 1 and 2

GENERAL LEDGER

Cash	Accounts Payable	Sales Discounts

Accts. Receivable	Notes Payable	Purchases

Prepaid Insurance	Sales	Purchase Returns and Allowances

Store Equipment	Sales Returns and Allowances	Purchase Discounts

ACCOUNTS RECEIVABLE SUBLEDGER

Jack Hertz	Trudy Stone	Dave Waylon

ACCOUNTS PAYABLE SUBLEDGER

Grass Corp.	McGrew Company	Sulter Inc.

Special Journal		Subledger	
Sales	S	Accounts Receivable ...	AR
Purchases.....................	P	Accounts Payable	AP
Cash Receipts	CR	Merchandise Inventory	MI
Cash Disbursements ...	CD	No Effect........................	NE
General Journal	G		

Date	Transaction	Special Journal	Subledger
Mar. 1	*Sold merchandise on credit.*	*S*	*AR/MI*
2	Defective merchandise sold on March 1 was returned by the customer. It was scrapped.		
3	Purchased office equipment on credit; terms n/30.		
5	Received payment regarding the March 1 sale.		
10	Received a credit memorandum from the supplier regarding defective equipment purchased on March 3.		
14	Sold merchandise for cash.		
16	Purchased merchandise inventory on credit; terms 1/5, n30.		
17	Paid the balance owing regarding the March 3 transaction.		
18	Purchased merchandise inventory for cash.		
21	Paid for the merchandise purchased on March 16.		
22	Sold old equipment for cash.		
30	Paid salaries for the month of March.		
30	Accrued utilities for the month of March.		
30	Closed the credit balance in the income summary to capital.		

Sales Journal — Page 3

Date	Account Debited	Invoice Number	PR	Accounts Receivable Dr. Sales Cr.	Cost of Goods Sold Dr. Merchandise Inventory Cr.

Cash Receipts Journal — Page 3

Date	Account Credited	PR	Explanation	Cash Dr.	Sales Disc. Dr.	Accts. Rec. Cr.	Sales Cr.	Other Accts. Cr.	COGS Dr. Merch. Inv. Cr.

Purchases Journal — Page 3

Date	Account	Date of Invoice	Terms	PR	Accounts Payable Cr.	Merch. Inventory Dr.	Office Supplies Dr.	Other Accounts Dr.

Cash Disbursements Journal — Page 3

Date	Ch. No.	Payee	Account Debited	PR	Cash Cr.	Merch. Inventory Cr.	Other Accounts Dr.	Accounts Payable Dr.

GENERAL JOURNAL   Page____

Date	Account Titles and Explanation	PR	Debit	Credit

Problem 8-3A   Part 1

ACCOUNTS RECEIVABLE SUBLEDGER

Paul Abrams   ACCOUNT NO. 106-1

DATE	EXPLANATION	PR	DEBIT	CREDIT	BALANCE

Linda Hobart   ACCOUNT NO. 106-2

DATE	EXPLANATION	PR	DEBIT	CREDIT	BALANCE

Kelly Schaefer   ACCOUNT NO. 106-3

DATE	EXPLANATION	PR	DEBIT	CREDIT	BALANCE

Part 2   ACCOUNTS PAYABLE SUBLEDGER

Frank's Supply   ACCOUNT NO. 201-1

DATE	EXPLANATION	PR	DEBIT	CREDIT	BALANCE

Baskin Company   ACCOUNT NO. 201-2

DATE	EXPLANATION	PR	DEBIT	CREDIT	BALANCE

Sprocket Company   ACCOUNT NO. 201-3

DATE	EXPLANATION	PR	DEBIT	CREDIT	BALANCE

Eau Claire Inc.   ACCOUNT NO. 201-4

DATE	EXPLANATION	PR	DEBIT	CREDIT	BALANCE

Part 3

				Sales Journal	Page
Date	Account Debited	Invoice Number	PR	Accounts Receivable Dr. Sales Cr.	Cost of Goods Sold Dr. Merchandise Inventory Cr.

				Cash Receipts Journal					Page	
Date	Accounts Credited	PR	Explanation	Cash Dr.	Sales Disc. Dr.	Accts. Rec. Cr.	Sales Cr.	Other Accts. Cr.	COGS Dr. Merch. Inv. Cr.

Purchases Journal								Page
Date	Account Credited	Date of Invoice	Terms	PR	Accounts Payable Cr.	Merch. Inventory Dr.	Office Supplies Dr.	Other Accounts Dr.

Cash Disbursements Journal								Page
Date	Ch. No.	Payee	Account Debited	PR	Cash Cr.	Merch. Inventory Cr.	Other Accounts Dr.	Accounts Payable Dr.

GENERAL JOURNAL   Page____

Date	Account Titles and Explanation	PR	Debit	Credit

GENERAL LEDGER

Cash   ACCOUNT NO. 101

DATE	EXPLANATION	PR	DEBIT	CREDIT	BALANCE
2011					
Mar. 31	Balance brought forward				167,000

Accounts Receivable   ACCOUNT NO. 106

DATE	EXPLANATION	PR	DEBIT	CREDIT	BALANCE

Merchandise Inventory   ACCOUNT NO. 119

DATE	EXPLANATION	PR	DEBIT	CREDIT	BALANCE
2011					
Mar. 31	Balance brought forward				95,000

Office Supplies   ACCOUNT NO. 124

DATE	EXPLANATION	PR	DEBIT	CREDIT	BALANCE

Store Supplies   ACCOUNT NO. 125

DATE	EXPLANATION	PR	DEBIT	CREDIT	BALANCE

Store Equipment   ACCOUNT NO. 165

DATE	EXPLANATION	PR	DEBIT	CREDIT	BALANCE

Accounts Payable
ACCOUNT NO. 201

DATE	EXPLANATION	PR	DEBIT	CREDIT	BALANCE

Long-Term Notes Payable
ACCOUNT NO. 251

DATE	EXPLANATION	PR	DEBIT	CREDIT	BALANCE
2011					
Mar. 31	Balance brought forward				167,000

Jeff Newton, Capital
ACCOUNT NO. 301

DATE	EXPLANATION	PR	DEBIT	CREDIT	BALANCE
2011					
Mar. 31	Balance brought forward				95,000

Sales
ACCOUNT NO. 413

DATE	EXPLANATION	PR	DEBIT	CREDIT	BALANCE

Sales Discounts
ACCOUNT NO. 415

DATE	EXPLANATION	PR	DEBIT	CREDIT	BALANCE

Cost of Goods Sold
ACCOUNT NO. 502

DATE	EXPLANATION	PR	DEBIT	CREDIT	BALANCE

Sales Salaries Expense
ACCOUNT NO. 621

DATE	EXPLANATION	PR	DEBIT	CREDIT	BALANCE

Advertising Expense   ACCOUNT NO. 655

DATE	EXPLANATION	PR	DEBIT	CREDIT	BALANCE

NOTE: For Parts 2 and 3, journalizing and posting, continue journalizing the transactions in the journals provided in Problem 8-3A.

Part 5

Trial Balance

	Debit	Credit

Schedule of Accounts Receivable

Schedule of Accounts Payable

Analysis component:

Parts 1, 2, 3

Sales Journal					Page 3
Date	Account Debited	Invoice Number	PR	Accounts Receivable Dr. Sales Cr.	Cost of Goods Sold Dr. Merchandise Inventory Cr.
2011					
Oct. 6	M. Craig	913	√	3,300	1,600
12	V. Foresman	914	√	3,650	1,900
15	A. Ihrig	915	√	3,100	1,700

Purchases Journal								Page 2
Date	Account	Date of Invoice	Terms	PR	Accounts Payable Cr.	Merch. Inventory Dr.	Office Supplies Dr.	Other Accounts Dr.
2011								
Oct. 2	Shore Co.	Oct. 2	2/10,n/60	√	3,200	3,200		
5	Brown Sup.	Oct. 3	n/10,EOM	√	1,300	1,300		
15	Shore Co.	Oct. 15	2/10,n/60	√	3,990	3,990		
15	Sunshine Co	Oct. 15	2/10,n/60	√	2,650	2,650		

Cash Receipts Journal								Page 3
Date	Account Credited	PR	Explanation	Cash Dr.	Sales Disc. Dr.	Accts. Rec. Cr.	Sales Cr.	Other Accts. Cr.	COGS Dr. Merch. Inv. Cr.
2011									
Oct. 2	B. Grigsby	√	Inv. 09/23	4,116	84	4,200			
15	Sales		Cash sales	38,830			38,830		21,400
15	M. Craig	√	Inv. 10/6	2,401	49	2,450			

Cash Disbursements Journal								Page 4
Date	Ch. No.	Payee	Account Debited	PR	Cash Cr.	Merch. Inventory Cr.	Other Accounts Dr.	Accounts Payable Dr.
2011								
Oct. 2	619	Omni Realty	Rent Exp.	640	2,250		2,250	
6	620	Fireside Co.	Fireside Co.	√	3,724	76		3,800
12	621	Shore Co.	Shore Co.	√	3,136	64		3,200
15	622	Jamie Green	Sales Sal. Exp.	621	2,020		2,020	

GENERAL JOURNAL

Date		Account Titles and Explanation	PR	Debit	Credit
2011					
Oct.	4	Accounts Payable—Fireside Company	201/√	460	
		Merchandise Inventory	119		460
		Received a credit memo for returns.			
	9	Sales Returns and Allowances	414	850	
		Accounts Receivable—Marge Craig	106/√		850
		Issued a credit memorandum.			
	9	Merchandise Inventory	119	430	
		Cost of Goods Sold	502		430
		Merchandise returned to inventory.			

ACCOUNTS RECEIVABLE SUBLEDGER

Marge Craig

DATE		EXPLANATION	PR	DEBIT	CREDIT	BALANCE
2011						
Oct.	6		S3	3,300		3,300
	9		G2		8,50	2,450
	15		CR3		2,450	-0-

Vickie Foresman

DATE		EXPLANATION	PR	DEBIT	CREDIT	BALANCE
2011						
Oct.	12		S3	3,650		3,650

Parts 2 and 3

Bill Grigsby

DATE	EXPLANATION	PR	DEBIT	CREDIT	BALANCE
2011					
Sept. 23		S2	4,200		4,200
Oct. 2		CR3		4,200	-0-

Amy Ihrig

DATE	EXPLANATION	PR	DEBIT	CREDIT	BALANCE
2011					
Oct. 15		S3	3,100		3,100

ACCOUNTS PAYABLE SUBLEDGER
Fireside Company

DATE	EXPLANATION	PR	DEBIT	CREDIT	BALANCE
2011					
Sept. 28		P1		4,260	4,260
Oct. 4		G2	460		3,800
6		CD4	3,800		-0-

Brown Supply Company

DATE	EXPLANATION	PR	DEBIT	CREDIT	BALANCE
2011					
Oct. 5		P2		1,300	1,300

Sunshine Company

DATE	EXPLANATION	PR	DEBIT	CREDIT	BALANCE
2011					
Oct. 15		P2		2,650	2,650

Parts 2 and 3   (Cont'd.)

Shore Company

DATE	EXPLANATION	PR	DEBIT	CREDIT	BALANCE
2011					
Oct. 2		P2		3,200	3,200
12		CD4	3,200		-0-
15		P2		3,990	3,990

Parts 2 and 3   GENERAL LEDGER

Cash   ACCOUNT NO. 101

DATE	EXPLANATION	PR	DEBIT	CREDIT	BALANCE
2011					
Sept. 30	Balance				5,361

Accounts Receivable   ACCOUNT NO. 106

DATE	EXPLANATION	PR	DEBIT	CREDIT	BALANCE
2011					
Sept. 30	Balance				4,200
Oct. 9		G2		850	3,350

Merchandise Inventory   ACCOUNT NO. 119

DATE	EXPLANATION	PR	DEBIT	CREDIT	BALANCE
2011					
Sept. 30	Balance				66,970
Oct. 4		G2		460	66,510
9		G2	430		66,940

Office Supplies   ACCOUNT NO. 124

DATE		EXPLANATION	PR	DEBIT	CREDIT	BALANCE
2011						
Sept.	30	Balance				607

Store Supplies   ACCOUNT NO. 125

DATE		EXPLANATION	PR	DEBIT	CREDIT	BALANCE
2011						
Sept.	30	Balance				346

Store Equipment   ACCOUNT NO. 165

DATE		EXPLANATION	PR	DEBIT	CREDIT	BALANCE
2011						
Sept.	30	Balance				42,129

Accumulated Depreciation, Store Equipment   ACCOUNT NO. 166

DATE		EXPLANATION	PR	DEBIT	CREDIT	BALANCE
2011						
Sept.	30	Balance				9,153

Accounts Payable   ACCOUNT NO. 201

DATE		EXPLANATION	PR	DEBIT	CREDIT	BALANCE
2011						
Sept.	30	Balance				4,260
Oct.	4		G2	460		3,800

Ken Shaw, Capital   ACCOUNT NO. 301

DATE		EXPLANATION	PR	DEBIT	CREDIT	BALANCE
2011						
Sept.	30	Balance				106,200

Ken Shaw, Withdrawals   ACCOUNT NO. 302

DATE	EXPLANATION	PR	DEBIT	CREDIT	BALANCE

Sales   ACCOUNT NO. 413

DATE	EXPLANATION	PR	DEBIT	CREDIT	BALANCE
2011					

Sales Returns and Allowances   ACCOUNT NO. 414

DATE	EXPLANATION	PR	DEBIT	CREDIT	BALANCE
2011					
Oct. 9		G2	850		850

Sales Discounts   ACCOUNT NO. 415

DATE	EXPLANATION	PR	DEBIT	CREDIT	BALANCE
2011					

Cost of Goods Sold   ACCOUNT NO. 502

DATE	EXPLANATION	PR	DEBIT	CREDIT	BALANCE
2011					
Oct. 9		G2		430	(430)

Sales Salaries Expense   ACCOUNT NO. 621

DATE	EXPLANATION	PR	DEBIT	CREDIT	BALANCE
2011					
Oct. 15		CD4	2,020		2,020

Rent Expense   ACCOUNT NO. 640

DATE	EXPLANATION	PR	DEBIT	CREDIT	BALANCE
2011					
Oct. 2		CD4	2,250		2,250

Utilities Expense   ACCOUNT NO. 690

DATE	EXPLANATION	PR	DEBIT	CREDIT	BALANCE
2011					

Part 4

SASKAN ENTERPRISES
Trial Balance
October 31, 2011

Part 4

SASKAN ENTERPRISES
Schedule of Accounts Receivable
October 31, 2011

SASKAN ENTERPRISES
Schedule of Accounts Payable
October 31, 2011

Problem 8-6A

		Sales Journal				Page
Date	Account Debited	Invoice Number	PR	Accounts Receivable Dr. Sales Cr.	PR	Cost of Goods Sold Dr. Merch. Inventory Cr.

		Purchases Journal						Page
Date	Account	Date of Invoice	Terms	PR	Accts. Payable Cr.	PR	Merch. Inventory Dr.	Office Supplies Dr.	Other Accounts Dr.

NOTE: An additional PR column has been added to both journals to facilitate the referencing of inventory entries into the inventory subsidiary ledger.

Date	PR	Purchases	Sales (at cost)	Inventory Balance

Note: An additional PR column has been added to the Inventory Subledger Record to facilitate referencing of inventory entries.

*Problem 8-7A

Part 1   ACCOUNTS RECEIVABLE SUBLEDGER

Paul Abrams   ACCOUNT NO. 106-1

DATE	EXPLANATION	PR	DEBIT	CREDIT	BALANCE

Linda Hobart   ACCOUNT NO. 106-2

DATE	EXPLANATION	PR	DEBIT	CREDIT	BALANCE

Kelly Schaefer   ACCOUNT NO. 106-3

DATE	EXPLANATION	PR	DEBIT	CREDIT	BALANCE

Part 2   ACCOUNTS PAYABLE SUBLEDGER

Frank's Supply   ACCOUNT NO. 201-1

DATE	EXPLANATION	PR	DEBIT	CREDIT	BALANCE

Baskin Company   ACCOUNT NO. 201-2

DATE	EXPLANATION	PR	DEBIT	CREDIT	BALANCE

Sprocket Company   ACCOUNT NO. 201-3

DATE	EXPLANATION	PR	DEBIT	CREDIT	BALANCE

Eau Claire Inc.					ACCOUNT NO. 201-4
DATE	EXPLANATION	PR	DEBIT	CREDIT	BALANCE

Part 3

Sales Journal   Page ____

Date	Account Debited	Invoice No.	PR	Accounts Receivable Dr. Sales Cr.

Cash Receipts Journal   Page ____

Date	Account Credited	PR	Explanation	Cash Dr.	Sales Disc. Dr.	Accts. Rec. Cr.	Sales Cr.	Other Accts. Cr.

Purchases Journal   Page

Date	Account Credited	Explanation	Cash Dr.	PR	Sales Disc. Dr.	Accounts Rec'ble Cr.	Sales Cr.	Other Accts. Cr.

Cash Disbursements Journal   Page

Date	Ch. No.	Payee	Account Debited	PR	Cash Cr.	Purch. Disc. Cr.	Other Accounts Dr.	Accts. Payable Dr.

GENERAL JOURNAL   Page____

Date	Account Titles and Explanation	PR	Debit	Credit

Parts 1 and 4   GENERAL LEDGER

Cash   ACCOUNT NO. 101

DATE	EXPLANATION	PR	DEBIT	CREDIT	BALANCE
2011					
Mar. 31					167,000

Accounts Receivable   ACCOUNT NO. 106

DATE	EXPLANATION	PR	DEBIT	CREDIT	BALANCE

Merchandise Inventory   ACCOUNT NO. 119

DATE	EXPLANATION	PR	DEBIT	CREDIT	BALANCE
2011					
Mar. 31					95,000

Office Supplies   ACCOUNT NO. 124

DATE	EXPLANATION	PR	DEBIT	CREDIT	BALANCE

Store Supplies   ACCOUNT NO. 125

DATE	EXPLANATION	PR	DEBIT	CREDIT	BALANCE

Store Equipment   ACCOUNT NO. 165

DATE	EXPLANATION	PR	DEBIT	CREDIT	BALANCE

Accounts Payable   ACCOUNT NO. 201

DATE	EXPLANATION	PR	DEBIT	CREDIT	BALANCE

Long-Term Notes Payable ACCOUNT NO. 251

DATE	EXPLANATION	PR	DEBIT	CREDIT	BALANCE
2011					
Mar. 31					167,000

Jeff Newton, Capital ACCOUNT NO. 301

DATE	EXPLANATION	PR	DEBIT	CREDIT	BALANCE
2011					
Mar. 31					95,000

Sales ACCOUNT NO. 413

DATE	EXPLANATION	PR	DEBIT	CREDIT	BALANCE

Sales Discounts ACCOUNT NO. 415

DATE	EXPLANATION	PR	DEBIT	CREDIT	BALANCE

Purchases ACCOUNT NO. 505

DATE	EXPLANATION	PR	DEBIT	CREDIT	BALANCE

Purchases Discounts ACCOUNT NO. 506

DATE	EXPLANATION	PR	DEBIT	CREDIT	BALANCE

Purchases Returns and Allowances ACCOUNT NO. 507

DATE	EXPLANATION	PR	DEBIT	CREDIT	BALANCE

Sales Salaries Expense   ACCOUNT NO. 621

DATE	EXPLANATION	PR	DEBIT	CREDIT	BALANCE

Advertising Expense   ACCOUNT NO. 655

DATE	EXPLANATION	PR	DEBIT	CREDIT	BALANCE

NOTE: For Parts 2 and 3, journalizing and posting, continue journalizing the transactions in the journals provided in *Problem 8-7A.

Part 5

Trial Balance

	Debit	Credit

Schedule of Accounts Receivable

Schedule of Accounts Payable

Special Journal		Subledger	
Sales	S	Accounts Receivable ...	AR
Purchases......................	P	Accounts Payable	AP
Cash Receipts..............	CR	Merchandise Inventory	MI
Cash Disbursements ...	CD	No Effect........................	NE
General Journal	G		

Date	Transaction	Special Journal	Subledger
May 1	The owner invested an automobile into the business.		
2	Sold merchandise and received cash.		
3	Purchased merchandise inventory on credit; terms 1/5, n30.		
4	Sold merchandise on credit.		
5	The customer of May 4 returned defective merchandise; the merchandise was scrapped.		
6	Regarding the May 3 purchase, received a credit memorandum from the supplier granting an allowance.		
15	Paid mid-month salaries.		
17	Purchased office supplies on credit; terms n/30.		
19	Paid for the balance owing on the May 3 purchase.		
22	Received payment on the May 4 sale.		
25	Borrowed money from bank.		
29	Purchased merchandise inventory; paid cash.		
30	Accrued interest revenue.		
30	Closed all revenue accounts to the Income Summary account.		

Sales Journal					Page 3
Date	Account Debited	Invoice Number	PR	Accounts Receivable Dr. Sales Cr.	Cost of Goods Sold Dr. Merchandise Inventory Cr.

Cash Receipts Journal									Page 3
Date	Accounts Credited	PR	Explanation	Cash Dr.	Sales Disc. Dr.	Accts. Rec. Cr.	Sales Cr.	Other Accts. Cr.	COGS Dr. Merch. Inv. Cr.

Purchases Journal								Page 3
Date	Account	Date of Invoice	Terms	PR	Accounts Payable Cr.	Merch. Inventory Dr.	Office Supplies Dr.	Other Accounts Dr.

Cash Disbursements Journal								Page 3
Date	Ch. No.	Payee	Account Debited	PR	Cash Cr.	Merch. Inventory Cr.	Other Accounts Dr.	Accounts Payable Dr.

GENERAL JOURNAL   Page____

Date	Account Titles and Explanation	PR	Debit	Credit

Problem 8-3B   Parts 2, 3, 5

Part 1   ACCOUNTS RECEIVABLE SUBLEDGER

Kelly Grody   ACCOUNT NO. 106-1

DATE	EXPLANATION	PR	DEBIT	CREDIT	BALANCE

Karen Harden   ACCOUNT NO. 106-2

DATE	EXPLANATION	PR	DEBIT	CREDIT	BALANCE

Paul Kane   ACCOUNT NO. 106-3

DATE	EXPLANATION	PR	DEBIT	CREDIT	BALANCE

Part 2   ACCOUNTS PAYABLE SUBLEDGER

Beech Company   ACCOUNT NO. 201-1

DATE	EXPLANATION	PR	DEBIT	CREDIT	BALANCE

Blackwater Inc.   ACCOUNT NO. 201-2

DATE	EXPLANATION	PR	DEBIT	CREDIT	BALANCE

Poppe's Supply   ACCOUNT NO. 201-3

DATE	EXPLANATION	PR	DEBIT	CREDIT	BALANCE

Sprague Company   ACCOUNT NO. 201-4

DATE	EXPLANATION	PR	DEBIT	CREDIT	BALANCE

Part 3

				Sales Journal	Page
Date	Account Debited	Invoice Number	PR	Accounts Receivable Dr. Sales Cr.	Cost of Goods Sold Dr. Merchandise Inventory Cr.

| | | | | Cash Receipts Journal | | | | | Page |
| | Account Credited | PR | Explanation | Cash Dr. | Sales Disc. Dr. | Accts. Rec. Cr. | Sales Cr. | Other Accts. Cr. | COGS Dr. Merch. Inv. Cr. |
Date									

| | | | | | Purchases Journal | | | Page |
Date	Account Credited	Date of Invoice	Terms	PR	Accounts Payable Cr.	Merch. Inventory Dr.	Office Supplies Dr.	Other Accounts Dr.

| | | | | | Cash Disbursements Journal | | | Page |
Date	Ch. No.	Payee	Account Debited	PR	Cash Cr.	Merch. Inventory Cr.	Other Accounts Dr.	Accounts Payable Dr.

GENERAL JOURNAL   Page____

Date	Account Titles and Explanation	PR	Debit	Credit

Problem 8-4B

Part 1   GENERAL LEDGER

Cash   ACCOUNT NO. 101

DATE	EXPLANATION	PR	DEBIT	CREDIT	BALANCE
2011					
Jun. 30	Balance brought forward				190,000

Accounts Receivable   ACCOUNT NO. 106

DATE	EXPLANATION	PR	DEBIT	CREDIT	BALANCE

Merchandise Inventory   ACCOUNT NO. 119

DATE	EXPLANATION	PR	DEBIT	CREDIT	BALANCE
2011					
Jun. 30	Balance brought forward				334,000

Office Supplies ACCOUNT NO. 124

DATE	EXPLANATION	PR	DEBIT	CREDIT	BALANCE

Store Supplies ACCOUNT NO. 125

DATE	EXPLANATION	PR	DEBIT	CREDIT	BALANCE

Store Equipment ACCOUNT NO. 165

DATE	EXPLANATION	PR	DEBIT	CREDIT	BALANCE

Accounts Payable ACCOUNT NO. 201

DATE	EXPLANATION	PR	DEBIT	CREDIT	BALANCE

Long-Term Notes Payable ACCOUNT NO. 251

DATE	EXPLANATION	PR	DEBIT	CREDIT	BALANCE
2011					
Jun. 30	Balance brought forward				334,000

Gene Duncan, Capital ACCOUNT NO. 301

DATE	EXPLANATION	PR	DEBIT	CREDIT	BALANCE
2011					
Jun. 30	Balance brought forward				190,000

Sales   ACCOUNT NO. 413

DATE	EXPLANATION	PR	DEBIT	CREDIT	BALANCE

Sales Discounts   ACCOUNT NO. 415

DATE	EXPLANATION	PR	DEBIT	CREDIT	BALANCE

Cost of Goods Sold   ACCOUNT NO. 502

DATE	EXPLANATION	PR	DEBIT	CREDIT	BALANCE

Sales Salaries Expense   ACCOUNT NO. 621

DATE	EXPLANATION	PR	DEBIT	CREDIT	BALANCE

Advertising Expense   ACCOUNT NO. 655

DATE	EXPLANATION	PR	DEBIT	CREDIT	BALANCE

NOTE: *For Parts 2 and 3, journalizing and posting, continue journalizing the transactions in the accounts provided in Problem 8-3A.*

Part 5

DUNCAN INDUSTRIES
Trial Balance
July 31, 2011

	Debit	Credit

DUNCAN INDUSTRIES
Schedule of Accounts Receivable
July 31, 2011

DUNCAN INDUSTRIES
Schedule of Accounts Payable
July 31, 2011

Analysis component: _____

_____

_____

_____

_____

_____

_____

_____

Problem 8-5B

Part 1

				Sales Journal	Page 3
Date	Account Debited	Invoice Number	PR	Accounts Receivable Dr. Sales Cr.	Cost of Goods Sold Dr. Merchandise Inventory Cr.
2011					
Oct. 6	M. Craig	913	√	6,600	3,600
12	H. Flatt	914	√	7,300	4,000
15	A. Izon	915	√	6,200	3,400

									COGS
			Cash Receipts Journal						Page 3
Date	Account Credited	PR	Explanation	Cash Dr.	Sales Disc. Dr.	Accts. Rec. Cr.	Sales Cr.	Other Accts. Cr.	Dr. Merch. Inv. Cr.
2011									
Oct. 2	J. Wildman	√	Inv. 09/23	8,232	168	8,400			
15	Sales		Cash sales	77,660			77,660		42,800
15	M. Craig	√	Inv. 10/6	4,802	98	4,900			

					Accounts Payable Cr.	Merch. Inventory Dr.	Office Supplies Dr.	Other Accounts Dr.

Purchases Journal — Page 2

Date	Account	Date of Invoice	Terms	PR	Accounts Payable Cr.	Merch. Inventory Dr.	Office Supplies Dr.	Other Accounts Dr.
2011								
Oct. 2	Walters Co.	10/2	2/10,n/60	√	6,400	6,400		
5	Green Supply	10/3	n/10,EOM	√	2,600	2,600		
15	Walters Co.	10/15	2/10,n/60	√	7,980	7,980		
15	Sunshine Co.	10/15	2/10,n/60	√	5,300	5,300		

Cash Disbursements Journal — Page 3

Date	Ch. No.	Payee	Account Debited	PR	Cash Cr.	Merch. Inventory Cr.	Other Accounts Dr.	Accounts Payable Dr.
2011								
Oct. 2	619	Omni Realty	Rent Exp.	640	4,500		4,500	
6	620	Fireside Co.	Fireside Co.	√	7,448	152		7,600
12	621	Walters Co.	Walters Co.	√	6,272	128		6,400
15	622	Jamie Ford	Sales Sal. Exp.	621	5,240		5,240	

GENERAL JOURNAL

Date		Account Titles and Explanation	PR	Debit	Credit
2011					
Oct.	4	Accounts Payable—Fireside Company	201/√	920	
		Merchandise Inventory	119		920
		Received a credit memo for returns.			
	9	Sales Returns and Allowances	414	1,700	
		Accounts Receivable—Marge Craig	106/√		1,700
		Issued a credit memorandum.			

ACCOUNTS RECEIVABLE SUBLEDGER

Marge Craig

DATE		EXPLANATION	PR	DEBIT	CREDIT	BALANCE
2011						
Oct.	6		S3	6,600		6,600
	9		G2		1,700	4,900
	15		CR3		4,900	-0-

Heather Flatt

DATE		EXPLANATION	PR	DEBIT	CREDIT	BALANCE
2011						
Oct.	12		S3	7,300		7,300

Amy Izon

DATE	EXPLANATION	PR	DEBIT	CREDIT	BALANCE
2011					
Oct. 15		S3	6,200		6,200

Jan Wildman

DATE	EXPLANATION	PR	DEBIT	CREDIT	BALANCE
2011					
Sept. 23		S2	8,400		8,400
Oct. 2		CR3		8,400	-0-

ACCOUNTS PAYABLE SUBLEDGER
Fireside Company

DATE	EXPLANATION	PR	DEBIT	CREDIT	BALANCE
2011					
Sept. 28		P1		8,520	8,520
Oct. 4		G2	920		7,600
6		CD4	7,600		-0-

Green Supply Company

DATE	EXPLANATION	PR	DEBIT	CREDIT	BALANCE
2011					
Oct. 5		P2		2,600	2,600

Sunshine Company

DATE	EXPLANATION	PR	DEBIT	CREDIT	BALANCE
2011					
Oct. 15		P2		5,300	5,300

Walters Company

DATE		EXPLANATION	PR	DEBIT	CREDIT	BALANCE
2011						
Oct.	2		P2		6,400	6,400
	12		CD4	6,400		-0-
	15		P2		7,980	7,980

Parts 2 and 3   **GENERAL LEDGER**

Cash   ACCOUNT NO. 101

DATE		EXPLANATION	PR	DEBIT	CREDIT	BALANCE
2011						
Sept.	30	Balance				10,722

Accounts Receivable   ACCOUNT NO. 106

DATE		EXPLANATION	PR	DEBIT	CREDIT	BALANCE
2011						
Sept.	30	Balance				8,400
Oct.	9		G2		1,700	6,700

Merchandise Inventory   ACCOUNT NO. 119

DATE		EXPLANATION	PR	DEBIT	CREDIT	BALANCE
2011						
Sept.	30	Balance				133,940
Oct.	4		G2		920	133,020

Office Supplies   ACCOUNT NO. 124

DATE		EXPLANATION	PR	DEBIT	CREDIT	BALANCE
2011						
Sept.	30	Balance				1,214

Store Supplies   ACCOUNT NO. 125

DATE		EXPLANATION	PR	DEBIT	CREDIT	BALANCE
2011						
Sept.	30	Balance				692

Store Equipment   ACCOUNT NO. 165

DATE		EXPLANATION	PR	DEBIT	CREDIT	BALANCE
2011						
Sept.	30	Balance				84,258

Accumulated Depreciation, Store Equipment   ACCOUNT NO. 166

DATE		EXPLANATION	PR	DEBIT	CREDIT	BALANCE
2011						
Sept.	30	Balance				18,306

Accounts Payable   ACCOUNT NO. 201

DATE		EXPLANATION	PR	DEBIT	CREDIT	BALANCE
2011						
Sept.	30	Balance				8,520
Oct.	4		G2	920		7,600

Marlee Levin, Capital   ACCOUNT NO. 301

DATE	EXPLANATION	PR	DEBIT	CREDIT	BALANCE
2011					
Sept. 30	Balance				212,400

Marlee Levin, Withdrawals   ACCOUNT NO. 302

DATE	EXPLANATION	PR	DEBIT	CREDIT	BALANCE
2011					

Sales   ACCOUNT NO. 413

DATE	EXPLANATION	PR	DEBIT	CREDIT	BALANCE
2011					

Sales Returns and Allowances   ACCOUNT NO. 414

DATE	EXPLANATION	PR	DEBIT	CREDIT	BALANCE
2011					
Oct. 9		G2	1,700		1,700

Sales Discounts   ACCOUNT NO. 415

DATE	EXPLANATION	PR	DEBIT	CREDIT	BALANCE
2011					

Cost of Goods Sold   ACCOUNT NO. 502

DATE	EXPLANATION	PR	DEBIT	CREDIT	BALANCE
2011					

Sales Salaries Expense   ACCOUNT NO. 621

DATE	EXPLANATION	PR	DEBIT	CREDIT	BALANCE
2011					
Oct. 15		CD4	5,240		5,240

Rent Expense   ACCOUNT NO. 640

DATE	EXPLANATION	PR	DEBIT	CREDIT	BALANCE
2011					
Oct. 2		CD4	4,500		4,500

Utilities Expense   ACCOUNT NO. 690

DATE	EXPLANATION	PR	DEBIT	CREDIT	BALANCE
2011					

Part 4

CHINA MOON PRODUCTS
Trial Balance
October 31, 2011

	Debit	Credit

CHINA MOON PRODUCTS
Schedule of Accounts Receivable
October 31, 2011

CHINA MOON PRODUCTS
Schedule of Accounts Payable
October 31, 2011

Problem 8-6B

		Sales Journal					Page
Date	Account Debited	Invoice Number	PR	Accounts Receivable Dr. Sales Cr.	PR	Cost of Goods Sold Dr. Merch. Inventory Cr.	

		Purchases Journal							Page
Date	Account Credited	Date of Invoice	Terms	PR	Accts. Payable Cr.	PR	Merch. Inventory Dr.	Office Supplies Dr.	Other Accounts Dr.

NOTE: *An additional PR column has been added to both journals to facilitate the referencing of inventory entries into the inventory subledger.*

Date	PR	Purchases	Sales (at cost)	Inventory Balance

Note: An additional PR column has been added to the Inventory Subledger Record to facilitate referencing of inventory entries.

*Problem 8-7B

Part 1   ACCOUNTS RECEIVABLE SUBLEDGER

Kelly Grody   ACCOUNT NO. 106-1

DATE	EXPLANATION	PR	DEBIT	CREDIT	BALANCE

Karen Harden   ACCOUNT NO. 106-2

DATE	EXPLANATION	PR	DEBIT	CREDIT	BALANCE

Paul Kane   ACCOUNT NO. 106-3

DATE	EXPLANATION	PR	DEBIT	CREDIT	BALANCE

Part 2   **ACCOUNTS PAYABLE SUBLEDGER**

Beech Company   ACCOUNT NO. 201-1

DATE	EXPLANATION	PR	DEBIT	CREDIT	BALANCE

Blackwater Inc.   ACCOUNT NO. 201-2

DATE	EXPLANATION	PR	DEBIT	CREDIT	BALANCE

Poppe's Supply   ACCOUNT NO. 201-3

DATE	EXPLANATION	PR	DEBIT	CREDIT	BALANCE

Sprague Company   ACCOUNT NO. 201-4

DATE	EXPLANATION	PR	DEBIT	CREDIT	BALANCE

Part 3

Sales Journal				Page
Date	Account Debited	Invoice No.	PR	Accounts Receivable Dr. Sales Cr.

Cash Receipts Journal								Page
Date	Account Credited	PR	Explanation	Cash Dr.	Sales Disc. Dr.	Accts. Rec. Cr.	Sales Cr.	Other Accts. Cr.

Purchases Journal								Page
Date	Account Credited	Date of Invoice	Terms	PR	Accts. Payable Cr.	Purchases Dr.	Office Supplies Dr.	Other Accts. Dr.

					Cash Disbursements Journal				Page	Accts.
Date	Ch. No.	Payee	Account Debited	PR	Cash Cr.	Purch. Disc. Cr.	Other Accounts Dr.	Payable Dr.

GENERAL JOURNAL   Page____

Date	Account Titles and Explanation	PR	Debit	Credit

*Problem 8-8B

Part 1   GENERAL LEDGER

Cash   ACCOUNT NO. 101

DATE	EXPLANATION	PR	DEBIT	CREDIT	BALANCE
2011					
Jun. 30	Balance brought forward				190,000

Accounts Receivable   ACCOUNT NO. 106

DATE	EXPLANATION	PR	DEBIT	CREDIT	BALANCE

Merchandise Inventory   ACCOUNT NO. 119

DATE	EXPLANATION	PR	DEBIT	CREDIT	BALANCE
2011					
Jun. 30	Balance brought forward				334,000

Office Supplies   ACCOUNT NO. 124

DATE	EXPLANATION	PR	DEBIT	CREDIT	BALANCE

Store Supplies   ACCOUNT NO. 125

DATE	EXPLANATION	PR	DEBIT	CREDIT	BALANCE

Store Equipment   ACCOUNT NO. 165

DATE	EXPLANATION	PR	DEBIT	CREDIT	BALANCE

Accounts Payable   ACCOUNT NO. 201

DATE	EXPLANATION	PR	DEBIT	CREDIT	BALANCE

Long-Term Notes Payable   ACCOUNT NO. 251

DATE	EXPLANATION	PR	DEBIT	CREDIT	BALANCE
2011					
Jun. 30	Balance brought forward				334,000

Gene Duncan, Capital   ACCOUNT NO. 301

DATE	EXPLANATION	PR	DEBIT	CREDIT	BALANCE
2011					
Jun. 30	Balance brought forward				190,000

Sales   ACCOUNT NO. 413

DATE	EXPLANATION	PR	DEBIT	CREDIT	BALANCE

Sales Discounts   ACCOUNT NO. 415

DATE	EXPLANATION	PR	DEBIT	CREDIT	BALANCE

Purchases   ACCOUNT NO. 505

DATE	EXPLANATION	PR	DEBIT	CREDIT	BALANCE

Purchase Discounts   ACCOUNT NO. 506

DATE	EXPLANATION	PR	DEBIT	CREDIT	BALANCE

Purchase Returns and Allowances   ACCOUNT NO. 507

DATE	EXPLANATION	PR	DEBIT	CREDIT	BALANCE

Sales Salaries Expense   ACCOUNT NO. 621

DATE	EXPLANATION	PR	DEBIT	CREDIT	BALANCE

Advertising Expense   ACCOUNT NO. 655

DATE	EXPLANATION	PR	DEBIT	CREDIT	BALANCE

*NOTE: For Parts 2 and 3, journalizing and posting, continue journalizing the transactions in the accounts provided in *Problem 8-7B.*

Part 5

DUNCAN INDUSTRIES
Trial Balance
July 31, 2011

	Debit	Credit

DUNCAN INDUSTRIES
Schedule of Accounts Receivable
July 31, 2011

DUNCAN INDUSTRIES
Schedule of Accounts Payable
July 31, 2011

Alpine Company - Perpetual

Sales Journal   Page 2

Date	Account Debited	Invoice Number	PR	Accounts Receivable Dr. Sales Cr.	Cost of Goods Sold Dr. Merchandise Inventory Cr.

Purchases Journal   Page 2

Date	Account	Date of Invoice	Terms	PR	Accounts Payable Cr.	Merch. Inventory Dr.	Office Supplies Dr.	Other Accounts Dr.

Cash Receipts Journal   Page 2

Date	Account Credited	PR	Explanation	Cash Dr.	Sales Disc. Dr.	Accts. Rec. Cr.	Sales Cr.	Other Accts. Cr.	COGS Dr. Merch. Inv. Cr.

Alpine Company - Perpetual (Continued)

| | | | | | | Merch. | Other | Accounts |
Date	Ch. No.	Payee	Account Debited	PR	Cash Cr.	Inventory Cr.	Accounts Dr.	Payable Dr.

Cash Disbursements Journal — Page 2

GENERAL JOURNAL   Page 3

Date	Account Titles and Explanation	PR	Debit	Credit

Alpine Company - Perpetual (Continued)

GENERAL JOURNAL   Page 3

Date		Account Titles and Explanation	PR	Debit	Credit

Name _____

Alpine Company - Perpetual (Continued)

Date	Account Titles and Explanation	PR	Debit	Credit

Cash   ACCOUNT NO. 101

DATE	EXPLANATION	PR	DEBIT	CREDIT	BALANCE
2011					
Apr. 30	Balance				50,247

Accounts Receivable   ACCOUNT NO. 106

DATE	EXPLANATION	PR	DEBIT	CREDIT	BALANCE
2011					
Apr. 30	Balance				4,725

Merchandise Inventory   ACCOUNT NO. 119

DATE	EXPLANATION	PR	DEBIT	CREDIT	BALANCE
2011					
Apr. 30	Balance				220,080

Office Supplies   ACCOUNT NO. 124

DATE	EXPLANATION	PR	DEBIT	CREDIT	BALANCE
2011					
Apr. 30	Balance				430

Store Supplies   ACCOUNT NO. 125

DATE	EXPLANATION	PR	DEBIT	CREDIT	BALANCE
2011					
Apr. 30	Balance				2,447

Alpine Company - Perpetual (Continued)

Prepaid Insurance   ACCOUNT NO. 128

DATE	EXPLANATION	PR	DEBIT	CREDIT	BALANCE
2011					
Apr. 30	Balance				3,318

Office Equipment   ACCOUNT NO. 163

DATE	EXPLANATION	PR	DEBIT	CREDIT	BALANCE
2011					
Apr. 30	Balance				22,470

Accumulated Depreciation, Office Equipment   ACCOUNT NO. 164

DATE	EXPLANATION	PR	DEBIT	CREDIT	BALANCE
2011					
Apr. 30	Balance				9,898

Store Equipment   ACCOUNT NO. 165

DATE	EXPLANATION	PR	DEBIT	CREDIT	BALANCE
2011					
Apr. 30	Balance				38,920

Accumulated Depreciation, Store Equipment   ACCOUNT NO. 166

DATE	EXPLANATION	PR	DEBIT	CREDIT	BALANCE
2011					
Apr. 30	Balance				17,556

Alpine Company - Perpetual (Continued)

Accounts Payable   ACCOUNT NO. 201

DATE	EXPLANATION	PR	DEBIT	CREDIT	BALANCE
2011					
Apr. 30	Balance				7,098

Clint Barry, Capital   ACCOUNT NO. 301

DATE	EXPLANATION	PR	DEBIT	CREDIT	BALANCE
2011					
Apr. 30	Balance				308,085

Clint Barry, Withdrawals   ACCOUNT NO. 302

DATE	EXPLANATION	PR	DEBIT	CREDIT	BALANCE
2011					

Sales   ACCOUNT NO. 413

DATE	EXPLANATION	PR	DEBIT	CREDIT	BALANCE

Sales Discounts   ACCOUNT NO. 414

DATE	EXPLANATION	PR	DEBIT	CREDIT	BALANCE

Alpine Company - Perpetual (Continued)

Sales Returns and Allowances   ACCOUNT NO. 415

DATE	EXPLANATION	PR	DEBIT	CREDIT	BALANCE

Cost of Goods Sold   ACCOUNT NO. 502

DATE	EXPLANATION	PR	DEBIT	CREDIT	BALANCE

Depreciation Expense, Office Equipment   ACCOUNT NO. 612

DATE	EXPLANATION	PR	DEBIT	CREDIT	BALANCE

Depreciation Expense, Store Equipment   ACCOUNT NO. 613

DATE	EXPLANATION	PR	DEBIT	CREDIT	BALANCE

Office Salaries Expense   ACCOUNT NO. 620

DATE	EXPLANATION	PR	DEBIT	CREDIT	BALANCE

Alpine Company - Perpetual (Continued)

Sales Salaries Expense   ACCOUNT NO. 621

DATE	EXPLANATION	PR	DEBIT	CREDIT	BALANCE

Insurance Expense   ACCOUNT NO. 637

DATE	EXPLANATION	PR	DEBIT	CREDIT	BALANCE

Rent Expense, Office Space   ACCOUNT NO. 641

DATE	EXPLANATION	PR	DEBIT	CREDIT	BALANCE

Rent Expense, Selling Space   ACCOUNT NO. 642

DATE	EXPLANATION	PR	DEBIT	CREDIT	BALANCE

Office Supplies Expense   ACCOUNT NO. 650

DATE	EXPLANATION	PR	DEBIT	CREDIT	BALANCE

Alpine Company - Perpetual (Continued)

Store Supplies Expense   ACCOUNT NO. 651

DATE	EXPLANATION	PR	DEBIT	CREDIT	BALANCE
2011					

Utilities Expense   ACCOUNT NO. 690

DATE	EXPLANATION	PR	DEBIT	CREDIT	BALANCE
2011					

Income Summary   ACCOUNT NO. 901

DATE	EXPLANATION	PR	DEBIT	CREDIT	BALANCE

ACCOUNTS RECEIVABLE LEDGER

NAME   Deaver Corp.

DATE	EXPLANATION	PR	DEBIT	CREDIT	BALANCE

NAME   Essex Company

DATE	EXPLANATION	PR	DEBIT	CREDIT	BALANCE

NAME   Nabors, Inc.

DATE	EXPLANATION	PR	DEBIT	CREDIT	BALANCE
2011					
Apr. 28		S2	4,725		4,725

Alpine Company - Perpetual (Continued)

NAME   Oscar Services.

DATE	EXPLANATION	PR	DEBIT	CREDIT	BALANCE
2011					

ACCOUNTS PAYABLE LEDGER

NAME   Chandler Corp.

DATE	EXPLANATION	PR	DEBIT	CREDIT	BALANCE
2011					

NAME   Gale, Inc.

DATE	EXPLANATION	PR	DEBIT	CREDIT	BALANCE
2011					

NAME   Parkay Products

DATE	EXPLANATION	PR	DEBIT	CREDIT	BALANCE
2011					
Apr. 29		P2		7,098	7,098

NAME   Thompson Supply Co.

DATE	EXPLANATION	PR	DEBIT	CREDIT	BALANCE

Alpine Company - Perpetual (Continued)

Alpine Company
Work Sheet
For Month Ended May 31, 2011

Account Titles	Trial Balance		Adjustments		Income Statement		Balance Sheet and Statement of Changes in Equity	
	Debit	Credit	Debit	Credit	Debit	Credit	Debit	Credit

Alpine Company - Perpetual (Continued)

Alpine Company
Income Statement
For Month Ended May 31, 2011

Alpine Company - Perpetual (Continued)

	Alpine Company	
	Statement of Changes in Equity	
	For Month Ended May 31, 2011	

	Alpine Company		
	Balance Sheet		
	May 31, 2011		

Alpine Company - Perpetual (Concluded)

Alpine Company
Post-Closing Trial Balance
May 31, 2011

	Debit	Credit

Alpine Company
Schedule of Accounts Receivable
May 31, 2011

Alpine Company
Schedule of Accounts Payable
May 31, 2011

Alpine Company - Periodic

Sales Journal				Page 2
Date	Account Debited	Invoice Number	PR	Accts. Receivable Dr. Sales Cr.

Purchases Journal								Page 2
Date	Account	Date of Inv.	Terms	PR	Accts. Pay. Cr.	Purchases Dr.	Office Supplies Dr.	Other Accts. Dr.

Cash Receipts Journal								Page 2
Date	Accounts Credited	Explanation	PR	Cash Dr.	Sales Disc. Dr.	Accts. Rec. Cr.	Sales Cr.	Other Accts. Cr.

Alpine Company - Periodic (Continued)

						Purch.	Other	Accts.
Cash Disbursements Journal								**Page 2**
Date	Ch. No.	Payee	Account Debited	PR	Cash Cr.	Purch. Disc. Cr.	Other Accts. Dr.	Accts. Payable Dr.

GENERAL JOURNAL   Page 3

Date	Account Titles and Explanation	PR	Debit	Credit

Alpine Company - Periodic (Continued)

	GENERAL JOURNAL			Page 3

Date	Account Titles and Explanation	PR	Debit	Credit

Alpine Company - Periodic (Continued)

GENERAL LEDGER

Cash   ACCOUNT NO. 101

DATE	EXPLANATION	PR	DEBIT	CREDIT	BALANCE
2011					
Apr. 30	Balance				50,247

Accounts Receivable   ACCOUNT NO. 106

DATE	EXPLANATION	PR	DEBIT	CREDIT	BALANCE
2011					
Apr. 30	Balance				4,725

Merchandise Inventory   ACCOUNT NO. 119

DATE	EXPLANATION	PR	DEBIT	CREDIT	BALANCE
2011					
Apr. 30	Balance				220,080

Office Supplies   ACCOUNT NO. 124

DATE	EXPLANATION	PR	DEBIT	CREDIT	BALANCE
2011					
Apr. 30	Balance				430

Store Supplies   ACCOUNT NO. 125

DATE	EXPLANATION	PR	DEBIT	CREDIT	BALANCE
2011					
Apr. 30	Balance				2,447

Alpine Company - Periodic (Continued)

Prepaid Insurance   ACCOUNT NO. 128

DATE	EXPLANATION	PR	DEBIT	CREDIT	BALANCE
2011					
Apr. 30	Balance				3,318

Office Equipment   ACCOUNT NO. 163

DATE	EXPLANATION	PR	DEBIT	CREDIT	BALANCE
2011					
Apr. 30	Balance				22,470

Accumulated Depreciation, Office Equipment   ACCOUNT NO. 164

DATE	EXPLANATION	PR	DEBIT	CREDIT	BALANCE
2011					
Apr. 30	Balance				9,898

Store Equipment   ACCOUNT NO. 165

DATE	EXPLANATION	PR	DEBIT	CREDIT	BALANCE
2011					
Apr. 30	Balance				38,920

Accumulated Depreciation, Store Equipment   ACCOUNT NO. 166

DATE	EXPLANATION	PR	DEBIT	CREDIT	BALANCE
2011					
Apr. 30	Balance				17,556

Alpine Company - Periodic (Continued)

Accounts Payable — ACCOUNT NO. 201

DATE	EXPLANATION	PR	DEBIT	CREDIT	BALANCE
2011					
Apr. 30	Balance				7,098

Clint Barry, Capital — ACCOUNT NO. 301

DATE	EXPLANATION	PR	DEBIT	CREDIT	BALANCE
2011					
Apr. 30	Balance				308,085

Clint Barry, Withdrawals — ACCOUNT NO. 302

DATE	EXPLANATION	PR	DEBIT	CREDIT	BALANCE
2011					

Sales — ACCOUNT NO. 413

DATE	EXPLANATION	PR	DEBIT	CREDIT	BALANCE

Sales Discounts — ACCOUNT NO. 414

DATE	EXPLANATION	PR	DEBIT	CREDIT	BALANCE

Sales Returns and Allowances — ACCOUNT NO. 415

DATE	EXPLANATION	PR	DEBIT	CREDIT	BALANCE

Alpine Company - Periodic (Continued)

Purchases   ACCOUNT NO. 505

DATE	EXPLANATION	PR	DEBIT	CREDIT	BALANCE

Purchases Discounts   ACCOUNT NO. 506

DATE	EXPLANATION	PR	DEBIT	CREDIT	BALANCE

Purchases Returns and Allowances   ACCOUNT NO. 507

DATE	EXPLANATION	PR	DEBIT	CREDIT	BALANCE

Depreciation Expense, Office Equipment   ACCOUNT NO. 612

DATE	EXPLANATION	PR	DEBIT	CREDIT	BALANCE

Depreciation Expense, Store Equipment   ACCOUNT NO. 613

DATE	EXPLANATION	PR	DEBIT	CREDIT	BALANCE

Office Salaries Expense   ACCOUNT NO. 620

DATE	EXPLANATION	PR	DEBIT	CREDIT	BALANCE

Alpine Company - Periodic (Continued)

Sales Salaries Expense   ACCOUNT NO. 621

DATE	EXPLANATION	PR	DEBIT	CREDIT	BALANCE

Insurance Expense   ACCOUNT NO. 637

DATE	EXPLANATION	PR	DEBIT	CREDIT	BALANCE

Rent Expense, Office Space   ACCOUNT NO. 641

DATE	EXPLANATION	PR	DEBIT	CREDIT	BALANCE

Rent Expense, Selling Space   ACCOUNT NO. 642

DATE	EXPLANATION	PR	DEBIT	CREDIT	BALANCE

Office Supplies Expense   ACCOUNT NO. 650

DATE	EXPLANATION	PR	DEBIT	CREDIT	BALANCE

Alpine Company - Periodic (Continued)

Store Supplies Expense   ACCOUNT NO. 651

DATE	EXPLANATION	PR	DEBIT	CREDIT	BALANCE
2011					

Utilities Expense   ACCOUNT NO. 690

DATE	EXPLANATION	PR	DEBIT	CREDIT	BALANCE
2011					

Income Summary   ACCOUNT NO. 901

DATE	EXPLANATION	PR	DEBIT	CREDIT	BALANCE

ACCOUNTS RECEIVABLE LEDGER

NAME   Deaver Corp.

DATE	EXPLANATION	PR	DEBIT	CREDIT	BALANCE

NAME   Essex Company

DATE	EXPLANATION	PR	DEBIT	CREDIT	BALANCE

NAME   Nabors, Inc.

DATE	EXPLANATION	PR	DEBIT	CREDIT	BALANCE
2011					
Apr. 28		S2	4,725		4,725

Alpine Company - Periodic (Continued)

NAME   Oscar Services.

DATE	EXPLANATION	PR	DEBIT	CREDIT	BALANCE
2011					

ACCOUNTS PAYABLE LEDGER

NAME   Chandler Corp.

DATE	EXPLANATION	PR	DEBIT	CREDIT	BALANCE
2011					

NAME   Gale, Inc.

DATE	EXPLANATION	PR	DEBIT	CREDIT	BALANCE
2011					

NAME   Parkay Products

DATE	EXPLANATION	PR	DEBIT	CREDIT	BALANCE
2011					
Apr. 29		P2		7,098	7,098

NAME   Thompson Supply Co.

DATE	EXPLANATION	PR	DEBIT	CREDIT	BALANCE

Alpine Company - Periodic (Continued)

Alpine Company
Work Sheet
For Month Ended May 31, 2011

Account Titles	Trial Balance		Adjustments		Income Statement		Balance Sheet and Statement of Changes in Equity	
	Debit	Credit	Debit	Credit	Debit	Credit	Debit	Credit

Alpine Company - Periodic (Continued)

Alpine Company
Income Statement
For Month Ended May 31, 2011

Alpine Company - Periodic (Continued)

Alpine Company		
Statement of Changes in Equity		
For Month Ended May 31, 2011		

Alpine Company			
Balance Sheet			
May 31, 2011			

Alpine Company - Periodic (Concluded)

Alpine Company
Post-Closing Trial Balance
May 31, 2011

	Debit	Credit

Alpine Company
Schedule of Accounts Receivable
May 31, 2011

Alpine Company
Schedule of Accounts Payable
May 31, 2011

(a) _____

_____

_____

_____

_____

_____

_____

(b) _____

_____

_____

_____

_____

_____

_____

(c) _____

_____

_____

_____

Quick Study 9-2

_____

_____

_____

_____

_____

_____

_____

_____

_____

_____

Quick Study 9-3

a. _____

_____

_____

_____

b. _____

_____

_____

_____

_____

(1) Establishment of the fund:

GENERAL JOURNAL   Page____

Date		Account Titles and Explanation	PR	Debit	Credit

(2) Summary of petty cash receipts and entry to reimburse the fund at month-end:

Wee Ones Agency
Petty Cash Payments Report
May 1 – 31, 2011

Receipts:
_____
_____
_____
_____
_____
_____

Fund total
Less: Cash remaining
Equals: Cash required to replenish petty cash
Cash over/(short)

GENERAL JOURNAL   Page____

Date		Account Titles and Explanation	PR	Debit	Credit

(3) _____
_____
_____
_____
_____

Name _____

GENERAL JOURNAL

Page____

Date	Account Titles and Explanation	PR	Debit	Credit

Quick Study 9-6

GENERAL JOURNAL

Page____

Date	Account Titles and Explanation	PR	Debit	Credit

GENERAL JOURNAL

Page____

Date	Account Titles and Explanation	PR	Debit	Credit

GENERAL JOURNAL   Page____

Date	Account Titles and Explanation	PR	Debit	Credit

Quick Study 9-9   Parts 1 and 2:

	Bank or Book Effect	Add or Subtract	Journal Entry Required or Not
(a)			
(b)			
(c)			
(d)			
(e)			
(f)			
(g)			

Bank Reconciliation

GENERAL JOURNAL   Page____

Date	Account Titles and Explanation	PR	Debit	Credit

Quick Study 9-11

_____
_____
_____
_____
_____
_____
_____
_____
_____
_____
_____
_____
_____
_____
_____
_____
_____
_____
_____

_____
_____
_____
_____
_____
_____
_____
_____
_____

Exercise 9-2

_____
_____
_____
_____
_____
_____
_____
_____
_____
_____
_____
_____

Exercise 9-3

(a) _____
_____
_____
_____
_____

(b) _____
_____
_____
_____
_____
_____

Internal Control Problem: _____

_____

_____

_____

_____

_____

_____

_____

Internal Control Recommendation: _____

_____

_____

_____

_____

Exercise 9-5

(a) Establish the Fund

GENERAL JOURNAL   Page____

Date	Account Titles and Explanation	PR	Debit	Credit

(b) Prepare a summary of petty cash receipts

Eanes Co.
Petty Cash Payments Report
January 1 – 8, 2011

Receipts: _____

_____

_____

_____

_____

Fund total _____

Less: Cash remaining _____

Equals: Cash required to replenish petty cash _____

Cash over/(short) _____

Record the reimbursement:

GENERAL JOURNAL   Page____

Date	Account Titles and Explanation	PR	Debit	Credit

Analysis component: _____

_____

_____

_____

_____

Exercise 9-6

(a) Establish the Fund

GENERAL JOURNAL   Page____

Date	Account Titles and Explanation	PR	Debit	Credit

(b) Prepare a summary of petty cash receipts

Brady Company
Petty Cash Payments Report
September 9 – 30, 2011

Receipts: _____

_____

_____

_____

_____

_____

Fund total _____

Less: Cash remaining _____

Equals: Cash required to replenish petty cash _____

Cash over/(short) _____

Reimburse and reduce the fund

GENERAL JOURNAL   Page____

Date	Account Titles and Explanation	PR	Debit	Credit

Analysis component:

_____

_____

_____

_____

_____

_____

_____

_____

GENERAL JOURNAL

Page____

Date	Account Titles and Explanation	PR	Debit	Credit
a.				
b.				
c.				

Exercise 9-8

GENERAL JOURNAL

Page____

Date	Account Titles and Explanation	PR	Debit	Credit

GENERAL JOURNAL   Page____

Date	Account Titles and Explanation	PR	Debit	Credit

Exercise 9-9

GENERAL JOURNAL   Page____

Date	Account Titles and Explanation	PR	Debit	Credit

GENERAL JOURNAL   Page____

Date		Account Titles and Explanation	PR	Debit	Credit

Analysis component:

_____
_____
_____
_____
_____
_____
_____
_____
_____
_____

_____

_____

2.

GENERAL JOURNAL   Page____

Date	Account Titles and Explanation	PR	Debit	Credit

Analysis component: _____

_____

_____

_____

Exercise 9-11

a. _____

_____

b.   GENERAL JOURNAL   Page____

Date	Account Titles and Explanation	PR	Debit	Credit

Analysis component:

_____

_____

_____

_____

_____

_____

_____

	Bank Balance		Book Balance			Not Shown on the Reconciliation
	Add	Deduct	Add	Deduct	Adjust	
1. Interest earned on the account.						
2. Deposit made on September 30 after the bank was closed.						
3. Cheques outstanding on August 31 that cleared the bank in September.						
4. NSF cheque from customer returned on September 15 but not recorded by the company.						
5. Cheques written and mailed to payees on September 30.						
6. Deposit made on September 5 that was processed on September 8.						
7. Bank service charge.						
8. Cheques written and mailed to payees on October 5.						
9. Cheque written by another depositor but charged against the company's account.						
10. Principal and interest collected by the bank but not recorded by the company.						
11. Special charge for collection of note in No. 10 on company's behalf.						
12. Cheque written against the account and cleared by the bank; not recorded by the bookkeeper.						

	Case X	Case Y	Case Z

Problem 9-1A

(1) Principle Violated:
Recommendation:

(2) Principle Violated:
Recommendation:

(3) Principle Violated:
Recommendation:

(4) Principle Violated:
Recommendation:

(5) Principle Violated:
Recommendation:

Part 1   GENERAL JOURNAL   Page____

Date	Account Titles and Explanation	PR	Debit	Credit

Part 2

Palladium Art Gallery
Petty Cash Payments Report
February 2 – 28, 2011

Receipts:
_____
_____
_____
_____
_____
_____
_____
_____
_____
_____
_____
_____
_____

Fund total
Less: Cash remaining
Equals: Cash required to replenish petty cash
Cash over/(short)

Part 3   GENERAL JOURNAL   Page____

Date	Account Titles and Explanation	PR	Debit	Credit

Analysis component: _____

_____

_____

_____

_____

_____

_____

_____

Problem 9-3A

Part 1   GENERAL JOURNAL   Page____

Date	Account Titles and Explanation	PR	Debit	Credit

Analysis component: _____

_____

_____

_____

_____

_____

a.

_____

b.   **GENERAL JOURNAL**   Page____

Date	Account Titles and Explanation	PR	Debit	Credit

Analysis component: _____

_____
_____
_____
_____
_____

a.

_____
_____
_____

b.

GENERAL JOURNAL   Page____

Date	Account Titles and Explanation	PR	Debit	Credit

GENERAL JOURNAL
Page____

Date	Account Titles and Explanation	PR	Debit	Credit

Problem 9-6A

Part 1

_____

_____

Part 2

GENERAL JOURNAL   Page____

Date	Account Titles and Explanation	PR	Debit	Credit

Analysis component: _____

_____

_____

_____

_____

_____

_____

_____

_____

_____

_____

_____

_____

Part 1

Part 2

GENERAL JOURNAL   Page____

Date	Account Titles and Explanation	PR	Debit	Credit

Analysis component: _____

_____
_____
_____
_____
_____
_____
_____
_____

Problem 9-8A

a.

Bank Statement Bal	36727.10	Book Statement B	35075.00
Add		Add	
Deposit of Sept 30	3,165.00	Interest earned	240.00
		Credit memo	2770.00
	39,892.60		
Deduct		Deduct	
Cheques no		NSF cheque	1
5893	968.5	1176-50	
5906	1718.6	cheque error	
5908	552.0	3239.10	600	
			36653.50

b.   GENERAL JOURNAL   Page____

Date	Account Titles and Explanation	PR	Debit	Credit

Problem 9-9A

a. _____

_____

b.   **GENERAL JOURNAL**   Page____

Date	Account Titles and Explanation	PR	Debit	Credit

Problem 9-10A

1.

_____
_____
_____

2.

GENERAL JOURNAL   Page____

Date		Account Titles and Explanation	PR	Debit	Credit

Analysis component:

(1) Principle Violated:
    Recommendation:

(2) Principle Violated:
    Recommendation:

(3) Principle Violated:
    Recommendation:

(4) Principle Violated:
    Recommendation:

(5) Principle Violated:
    Recommendation:

Part 1   **GENERAL JOURNAL**   Page____

Date	Account Titles and Explanation	PR	Debit	Credit

Part 2

Dack & Blecker Company
Petty Cash Payments Report
July 5 – 31, 2011

Receipts: _____

_____

_____

_____

_____

_____

_____

_____

_____

_____

_____

_____

_____

_____

Fund total

Less: Cash remaining

Equals: Cash required to replenish petty cash _____

Cash over/(short)

Part 3   **GENERAL JOURNAL**   Page____

Date	Account Titles and Explanation	PR	Debit	Credit

Analysis component: _____

_____
_____
_____
_____
_____
_____
_____
_____

Problem 9-3B

GENERAL JOURNAL   Page____

Date	Account Titles and Explanation	PR	Debit	Credit

Analysis component: _____

_____
_____
_____
_____
_____
_____

a.

_____

_____

_____

b.   **GENERAL JOURNAL**   Page____

Date	Account Titles and Explanation	PR	Debit	Credit

Analysis component: _____

_____

_____

_____

_____

_____

_____

_____

_____

_____

_____

a.

_____

GENERAL JOURNAL   Page____

Date		Account Titles and Explanation	PR	Debit	Credit

Part 1

_____

GENERAL JOURNAL   Page____

Date	Account Titles and Explanation	PR	Debit	Credit

Analysis component: _____

_____
_____
_____
_____
_____
_____
_____
_____
_____
_____

Problem 9-7B   Part 1

_____
_____

GENERAL JOURNAL   Page____

Date	Account Titles and Explanation	PR	Debit	Credit

GENERAL JOURNAL   Page____

Date	Account Titles and Explanation	PR	Debit	Credit

Analysis component:

_____

_____

_____

_____

_____

_____

_____

_____

_____

_____

_____

Problem 9-8B   Part 1

_____

_____

GENERAL JOURNAL   Page____

Date	Account Titles and Explanation	PR	Debit	Credit

Problem 9-9B   Part 1

Part 2   GENERAL JOURNAL   Page____

Date	Account Titles and Explanation	PR	Debit	Credit

Problem 9-10B   Part 1

2.

GENERAL JOURNAL   Page____

Date	Account Titles and Explanation	PR	Debit	Credit

Analysis component: _____

_____
_____
_____
_____
_____
_____

GENERAL JOURNAL

Date		Account Titles and Explanation	PR	Debit	Credit

Quick Study 10-2

GENERAL JOURNAL

Date		Account Titles and Explanation	PR	Debit	Credit

GENERAL JOURNAL

Date	Account Titles and Explanation	PR	Debit	Credit

Quick Study 10-3

Biatech
Partial Balance Sheet
December 31, 2011

GENERAL JOURNAL

Date		Account Titles and Explanation	PR	Debit	Credit

Quick Study 10-5

Allowance for Doubtful Accounts

GENERAL JOURNAL   Page____

Date		Account Titles and Explanation	PR	Debit	Credit

Quick Study 10-6

a.   ## GENERAL JOURNAL   Page____

Date		Account Titles and Explanation	PR	Debit	Credit

b. _____

c. _____

Name _____

GENERAL JOURNAL

Page____

Date	Account Titles and Explanation	PR	Debit	Credit

Allowance for Doubtful Accounts

Quick Study 10-8

GENERAL JOURNAL

Page____

Date	Account Titles and Explanation	PR	Debit	Credit

Quick Study 10-9

GENERAL JOURNAL

Page____

Date	Account Titles and Explanation	PR	Debit	Credit

GENERAL JOURNAL

Date	Account Titles and Explanation	PR	Debit	Credit

Quick Study 10-11

GENERAL JOURNAL

Date	Account Titles and Explanation	PR	Debit	Credit

^Quick Study 10-12

GENERAL JOURNAL

Date	Account Titles and Explanation	PR	Debit	Credit

GENERAL JOURNAL

Date	Account Titles and Explanation	PR	Debit	Credit

Calculations:

_____
_____
_____
_____
_____
_____
_____

*Quick Study 10-14

a. _____
b. _____
c. _____

Part 1

GENERAL LEDGER

Accounts Receivable	Sales	Sales Returns and Allowances

ACCOUNTS RECEIVABLE SUBLEDGER

ABC Shop	Colt Enterprises	Red McKenzie

Part 2

Comparison:

GENERAL JOURNAL

Date	Account Titles and Explanation	PR	Debit	Credit

Exercise 10-3

GENERAL JOURNAL

Date	Account Titles and Explanation	PR	Debit	Credit

a.

Accounts Receivable	Allowance for Doubtful Accounts

GENERAL JOURNAL

Date	Account Titles and Explanation	PR	Debit	Credit

b.

Accounts Receivable	Allowance for Doubtful Accounts

GENERAL JOURNAL

Date	Account Titles and Explanation	PR	Debit	Credit

Exercise 10-5

a. _____

b. _____

c. _____

d. _____

e. _____

Partial Balance Sheet

Exercise 10-7

a, b, and c   **GENERAL JOURNAL**   Page____

Date	Account Titles and Explanation	PR	Debit	Credit

a, b, and c (cont'd.)   **GENERAL JOURNAL**   Page____

Date	Account Titles and Explanation	PR	Debit	Credit

Calculations:

Accounts Receivable   Allowance for Doubtful Accounts

d.

Partial Balance Sheet

Analysis component:

_____
_____
_____
_____
_____
_____
_____

Date	Account Titles and Explanation	PR	Debit	Credit

Calculations:

Accounts Receivable	Allowance for Doubtful Accounts

d.

Partial Balance Sheet		

Analysis component:

_____

_____

_____

_____

_____

Exercise 10-9

a and b.   GENERAL JOURNAL   Page____

Date	Account Titles and Explanation	PR	Debit	Credit

Calculations:

Accounts Receivable	Allowance for Doubtful Accounts

c.

Partial Balance Sheet

Analysis component:

_____
_____
_____
_____
_____

Exercise 10-10

GENERAL JOURNAL   Page____

Date	Account Titles and Explanation	PR	Debit	Credit

Analysis component:

_____
_____
_____
_____
_____
_____
_____
_____

GENERAL JOURNAL

Date	Account Titles and Explanation	PR	Debit	Credit

Exercise 10-12

GENERAL JOURNAL

Date	Account Titles and Explanation	PR	Debit	Credit

GENERAL JOURNAL

Date	Account Titles and Explanation	PR	Debit	Credit

GENERAL JOURNAL

Date	Account Titles and Explanation	PR	Debit	Credit

Financial Statement Note(s):

_____

_____

_____

_____

GENERAL JOURNAL

Date	Account Titles and Explanation	PR	Debit	Credit

Calculations:

_____

_____

_____

_____

_____

_____

*Exercise 10-16

Part 1

Accounts Receivable Turnover	Days' Sales Uncollected

_____

_____

_____

_____

_____

_____

_____

Part 2

_____

_____

_____

_____

_____

_____

_____

_____

a. Expense is 2% of credit sales:

GENERAL JOURNAL

Date	Account Titles and Explanation	PR	Debit	Credit

b. Allowance is 5% of accounts receivable:

GENERAL JOURNAL

Date	Account Titles and Explanation	PR	Debit	Credit

Calculations for Part b:

**Allowance for
Doubtful Accounts**

Part 2

Part 3

Analysis component:

_____
_____
_____
_____
_____
_____

Calculation of the required balance of the allowance (using an aging analysis):

_____
_____
_____
_____
_____
_____
_____

Allowance for Doubtful Accounts

Part 2

GENERAL JOURNAL

Date	Account Titles and Explanation	PR	Debit	Credit

Analysis component:

_____
_____
_____
_____
_____
_____

GENERAL JOURNAL

Page____

Date	Account Titles and Explanation	PR	Debit	Credit

Part 2

GENERAL JOURNAL   Page____

Date	Account Titles and Explanation	PR	Debit	Credit

Part 3

Part 4

_____

_____

Part 5

GENERAL JOURNAL   Page____

Date	Account Titles and Explanation	PR	Debit	Credit

Calculations:

Accounts Receivable	Allowance for Doubtful Accounts

Part 6

Part 7

_____

_____

GENERAL JOURNAL

Date	Account Titles and Explanation	PR	Debit	Credit
2011				
a.				
b.				
c.				
d.				

Calculations:

Accounts Receivable	Allowance for Doubtful Accounts

GENERAL JOURNAL

Date	Account Titles and Explanation	PR	Debit	Credit
2012				
e.				
f.				
g.				
h.				

Calculations:

Accounts Receivable	Allowance for Doubtful Accounts

Name _____

Part a

GENERAL JOURNAL

Date	Account Titles and Explanation	PR	Debit	Credit
2011				

_____ **Allowance for Doubtful Accounts** _____

Part b

Part c

GENERAL JOURNAL

Date	Account Titles and Explanation	PR	Debit	Credit
2011				

Calculations:

_____ **Allowance for Doubtful Accounts** _____

Part d

Part 1

GENERAL JOURNAL

Date	Account Titles and Explanation	PR	Debit	Credit

Part 2

GENERAL JOURNAL

Date	Account Titles and Explanation	PR	Debit	Credit

Calculations:

Accounts Receivable	Allowance for Doubtful Accounts

Problem 10-7A

a.

Month

Customer	Not yet due 0.5%	1 to 29 days past due 1%	30 to 59 days past due 4%	60 to 89 days past due 10%	90 to 119 days past due 20%	Over 119 days past due 50%
B. Axley						
T. Holton						
W. Nix						
C. Percy						
K. Willis						

b.   GENERAL JOURNAL   Page____

Date	Account Titles and Explanation	PR	Debit	Credit

Calculations:

Accounts Receivable	Allowance for Doubtful Accounts

Problem 10-8A

a.   GENERAL JOURNAL   Page____

Date	Account Titles and Explanation	PR	Debit	Credit
2011				
2012				
2013				

Calculations:

Accounts Receivable	Allowance for Doubtful Accounts

Analysis component:

_____
_____
_____
_____
_____

Problem 10-9A

Parts a, b, and c.

Date of Note	Principal	Interest Rate	Term	Maturity Date	Days of Accrued Interest at Dec. 31, 2011	Accrued Interest at Dec. 31, 2011
Nov. 1/10	$240,000	7%	180 days			
Jan. 5/11	100,000	8%	90 days			
Nov. 20/11	90,000	10%	45 days			
Dec. 10/11	120,000	12%	30 days			

Calculations:

_____
_____
_____
_____
_____
_____
_____
_____
_____
_____
_____
_____
_____
_____
_____
_____

d.   GENERAL JOURNAL   Page____

Date		Account Titles and Explanation	PR	Debit	Credit

e.   GENERAL JOURNAL   Page____

Date		Account Titles and Explanation	PR	Debit	Credit

Problem 10-10A

a.   GENERAL JOURNAL   Page____

Date		Account Titles and Explanation	PR	Debit	Credit

GENERAL JOURNAL   Page____

Date	Account Titles and Explanation	PR	Debit	Credit

b. Determine the maturity date of the note dated March 2:

_____

_____

_____

_____

_____

Prepare the entry on the maturity date:

GENERAL JOURNAL   Page____

Date	Account Titles and Explanation	PR	Debit	Credit

Parts (a) to (f)

GENERAL JOURNAL   Page____

Date	Account Titles and Explanation	PR	Debit	Credit

Analysis component:

_____

_____

_____

_____

_____

_____

GENERAL JOURNAL

Page____

Date	Account Titles and Explanation	PR	Debit	Credit

Analysis component: _____

_____

_____

_____

_____

_____

GENERAL JOURNAL   Page____

Date	Account Titles and Explanation	PR	Debit	Credit

GENERAL JOURNAL   Page____

Date		Account Titles and Explanation	PR	Debit	Credit

a. Expense is 2.5% of credit sales:

GENERAL JOURNAL

Date	Account Titles and Explanation	PR	Debit	Credit

b. Allowance is 6% of accounts receivable:

GENERAL JOURNAL

Date	Account Titles and Explanation	PR	Debit	Credit

Calculations for Part b:

Allowance for Doubtful Accounts

Part 2

Part 3

Analysis component:

_____
_____
_____
_____
_____
_____
_____

Calculation of the required balance of the allowance (using an aging analysis):

_____
_____
_____
_____
_____
_____
_____

Allowance for Doubtful Accounts

Part 2

GENERAL JOURNAL

Date	Account Titles and Explanation	PR	Debit	Credit

Analysis component:

_____
_____
_____
_____
_____
_____

GENERAL JOURNAL   Page____

Date	Account Titles and Explanation	PR	Debit	Credit

Part 2

GENERAL JOURNAL   Page____

Date	Account Titles and Explanation	PR	Debit	Credit

Part 3

Part 4

_____

_____

Part 5

GENERAL JOURNAL   Page____

Date	Account Titles and Explanation	PR	Debit	Credit

Calculations:

Accounts Receivable	Allowance for Doubtful Accounts

Part 6

Part 7

_____

_____

Name _____

GENERAL JOURNAL

Date	Account Titles and Explanation	PR	Debit	Credit
2011				
a.				
b.				
c.				
d.				

Calculations:

Accounts Receivable

Allowance for Doubtful Accounts

GENERAL JOURNAL

Date	Account Titles and Explanation	PR	Debit	Credit
2012				
e.				
f.				
g.				
h.				

Calculations:

Accounts Receivable

Allowance for Doubtful Accounts

Name _____

Part a

GENERAL JOURNAL

Date	Account Titles and Explanation	PR	Debit	Credit
2011				

Allowance for Doubtful Accounts

Part b

Part c

GENERAL JOURNAL

Date	Account Titles and Explanation	PR	Debit	Credit
2011				

Calculations:

Allowance for Doubtful Accounts

Part d

Name _____

Part 1

GENERAL JOURNAL

Date	Account Titles and Explanation	PR	Debit	Credit

Part 2

GENERAL JOURNAL

Date	Account Titles and Explanation	PR	Debit	Credit

Calculations:

Accounts Receivable	Allowance for Doubtful Accounts

Problem 10-7B

a.

Month

Customer	Not yet due 1%	1 to 29 days past due 2%	30 to 59 days past due 5%	60 to 89 days past due 20%	90 to 119 days past due 35%	Over 119 days past due 50%
A. Leslie						
T. Meston						
P. Obrian						
L. Timms						
W. Victor						

b.   GENERAL JOURNAL   Page____

Date	Account Titles and Explanation	PR	Debit	Credit

Calculations:

Accounts Receivable	Allowance for Doubtful Accounts

Problem 10-8B

a.   GENERAL JOURNAL   Page____

Date	Account Titles and Explanation	PR	Debit	Credit
2011				
2012				
2013				

Calculations:

Accounts Receivable	Allowance for Doubtful Accounts

Analysis component:

_____
_____
_____
_____
_____

Problem 10-9B

Parts a, b, and c.

Date of Note	Principal	Interest Rate	Term	Maturity Date	Days of Accrued Interest at Dec. 31, 2011	Accrued Interest at Dec. 31, 2011
Sept. 20/10	$490,000	7%	120 days			
June 01/11	240,000	9%	45 days			
Nov. 23/11	164,000	9%	90 days			
Dec. 18/11	120,000	10%	30 days			

Calculations:

_____
_____
_____
_____
_____
_____
_____
_____
_____
_____
_____
_____
_____
_____
_____
_____
_____

d.   GENERAL JOURNAL   Page____

Date	Account Titles and Explanation	PR	Debit	Credit

e.   GENERAL JOURNAL   Page____

Date	Account Titles and Explanation	PR	Debit	Credit

Problem 10-10B

a.   GENERAL JOURNAL   Page____

Date	Account Titles and Explanation	PR	Debit	Credit

GENERAL JOURNAL   Page____

Date	Account Titles and Explanation	PR	Debit	Credit

b. Determine the maturity date of the note dated March 1:

_____

_____

_____

_____

_____

_____

Prepare the entry on the maturity date:

GENERAL JOURNAL   Page____

Date	Account Titles and Explanation	PR	Debit	Credit

Parts (a) to (f)

GENERAL JOURNAL   Page____

Date	Account Titles and Explanation	PR	Debit	Credit

Analysis component: _____

_____

_____

_____

_____

_____

GENERAL JOURNAL

Page____

Date	Account Titles and Explanation	PR	Debit	Credit

Analysis component: _____
_____
_____
_____
_____

Name _____

GENERAL JOURNAL

Page____

Date	Account Titles and Explanation	PR	Debit	Credit

GENERAL JOURNAL   Page____

Date	Account Titles and Explanation	PR	Debit	Credit

_____
_____
_____
_____
_____
_____
_____

Quick Study 11-2

GENERAL JOURNAL

Date		Account Titles and Explanation	PR	Debit	Credit

Quick Study 11-3

GENERAL JOURNAL

Date		Account Titles and Explanation	PR	Debit	Credit

Quick Study 11-4

Employee	Gross Pay	Deductions				Pay		Distribution	
		EI Premium	Taxes	CPP	Deductions Total	Net Pay		Office Salaries	Sales Salaries
Johnson, S.	1,200.00	20.76	279.05	56.07					
Waverley, N.	530.00	9.17	69.00	22.90					
Zender, B.	675.00	11.68	105.00	30.08					
Totals	2,405.00	41.61	453.05	109.05					

| Employee | Gross Pay | Deductions | | | | Pay | Salaries Expense |
		EI Premium	Taxes	CPP	Total Deductions	Net Pay	
Bentley, A.	2,010.00						
Craig, T.	2,115.00						
Totals	4,125.00						

Quick Study 11-6

| Employee | Gross Pay | Deductions | | | | Pay | Distribution | |
		EI Premium	Income Taxes	CPP	Total Deductions	Net Pay	Office Salaries	Sales Salaries
Withers, S.	2,500.00						2,500.00	
Volt. C.	1,800.00							1,800.00
Totals								

Calculations:

_____
_____
_____
_____
_____
_____
_____
_____

Quick Study 11-7

GENERAL JOURNAL   Page____

Date	Account Titles and Explanation	PR	Debit	Credit

GENERAL JOURNAL

Date	Account Titles and Explanation	PR	Debit	Credit

Quick Study 11-9

GENERAL JOURNAL

Date	Account Titles and Explanation	PR	Debit	Credit

Quick Study 11-10

GENERAL JOURNAL

Date	Account Titles and Explanation	PR	Debit	Credit

GENERAL JOURNAL

Date	Account Titles and Explanation	PR	Debit	Credit

Exercise 11-1

Exercise 11-2

Employee	Gross Pay	EI Premium	Income Taxes	CPP	Health Insurance	Total Deductions	Net Pay
				Deductions			Pay
H. Chea	720.00		115.50		24.00		
J. Lim	610.00		88.30		24.00		
D. Patelli	830.00		148.95		36.00		
S. Quinata	1,700.00		460.70		24.00		
Totals	3,860.00		813.45		108.00		

Calculations:

_____

_____

_____

_____

_____

_____

_____

GENERAL JOURNAL

Date	Account Titles and Explanation	PR	Debit	Credit

Exercise 11-3

Employee	Gross Pay	EI Prem.	Income Taxes	United Way	CPP	Total Deductions	Net Pay	Admin. Salaries	Sales Salaries
Akerley, D.	1,900.00	32.87	381.95	80.00	87.39				
Nesbitt, M.	1,260.00	21.80	187.95	50.00	55.71				
Trent, F.	1,680.00	29.06	304.85	40.00	76.50				
Vacon, M.	3,000.00	51.90	768.50	300.00	141.84				
Total	7,840.00	135.63	1,643.25	470.00	361.44				

Exercise 11-4

Employee	Gross Pay	EI Prem.	Income Taxes	Canada Savings Bonds	CPP	United Way	Total Deductions	Net Pay	Office Salaries	Sales Salaries
Crimson	1,995.00								1,995.00	
Long	2,040.00									2,040.00
Morris	2,000.00									2,000.00
Peterson	2,280.00									2,280.00
Totals										

Name _____

Employee	Gross Pay	EI Prem.	Income Taxes	Medical Ins.	CPP	United Way	Total Deductions	Net Pay	Office Salaries	Guide Salaries
			Deductions					**Payment**	**Distribution**	
Wynne	1,200.00			65.00		40.00				1,200.00
Short	950.00			65.00		100.00			950.00	
Pearl	1,150.00			65.00		0				1,150.00
Quince	875.00			65.00		50.00				875.00
Totals										

Calculations:

_____
_____
_____
_____
_____
_____
_____
_____
_____

Exercise 11-6

GENERAL JOURNAL

Date	Account Titles and Explanation	PR	Debit	Credit

GENERAL JOURNAL

Date		Account Titles and Explanation	PR	Debit	Credit

Exercise 11-8

GENERAL JOURNAL

Date		Account Titles and Explanation	PR	Debit	Credit

Exercise 11-9

GENERAL JOURNAL

Date		Account Titles and Explanation	PR	Debit	Credit

GENERAL JOURNAL

Date		Account Titles and Explanation	PR	Debit	Credit

Exercise 11-11

Employee	CPP Contribution	EI Contribution	Retirement Fund Contributions	Health Insurance

Calculations:

_____

_____

_____

_____

_____

_____

_____

_____

_____

_____

GENERAL JOURNAL

Date	Account Titles and Explanation	PR	Debit	Credit

Exercise 11-13

GENERAL JOURNAL

Date	Account Titles and Explanation	PR	Debit	Credit

Part 1

Employee	Daily Time							Total Hrs.	O.T. Hrs.	Reg. Pay Rate	Earnings		
	M	T	W	T	F	S	S				Regular Pay	O.T. Premium Pay	Gross Pay
Loran	8	8	8	8	8	4	0			40.00			
Sousa	7	8	6	7	8	4	0			36.00			
Smith	8	8	0	8	8	4	4			32.00			
Parton	8	8	8	8	8	0	0			40.00			
Wood	0	6	6	6	6	8	8			36.00			

Employee	Deductions						Payment	Distribution	
	EI Prem.	CPP	Income Tax	Hosp. Ins.	Union Dues	Total Deductions	Net Pay	Office Salaries Expense	Service Wages Expense
Loran				40.00	16.00				
Sousa				40.00	15.00				
Smith				40.00	14.00				
Parton				40.00	16.00				
Wood				40.00	15.00				
Totals				200.00	76.00				

Part 2

GENERAL JOURNAL

Date	Account Titles and Explanation	PR	Debit	Credit

Part 1

GENERAL JOURNAL

Date	Account Titles and Explanation	PR	Debit	Credit

Part 2

GENERAL JOURNAL

Date	Account Titles and Explanation	PR	Debit	Credit

Problem 11-3A

Part 1

GENERAL JOURNAL

Date	Account Titles and Explanation	PR	Debit	Credit

Part 2

GENERAL JOURNAL

Date	Account Titles and Explanation	PR	Debit	Credit

Part 3

GENERAL JOURNAL

Date	Account Titles and Explanation	PR	Debit	Credit

Problem 11-4A

GENERAL JOURNAL

Date	Account Titles and Explanation	PR	Debit	Credit

GENERAL JOURNAL

Date	Account Titles and Explanation	PR	Debit	Credit

Part 1

Employee	M	T	W	T	F	S	S	Total Hrs.	O.T. Hrs.	Reg. Pay Rate	Regular Pay	O.T. Premium Pay	Gross Pay
			Daily Time									Earnings	
Amoko	8	8	8	8	8	0	0			34.00			
Carson	7	8	8	7	8	4	0			36.00			
De	8	8	0	8	8	4	4			36.00			
Deszca	8	8	8	8	8	0	0			30.00			
Tan	0	6	6	6	6	8	8			30.00			

Employee	EI Prem.	CPP	Income Tax	Hosp. Ins.	Union Dues	Total Deductions	Net Pay	Office Salaries Expense	Service Wages Expense
			Deductions				Payment	Distribution	
Amoko				30.00	12.00				
Carson				30.00	12.00				
De				30.00	12.00				
Deszca				30.00	12.00				
Tan				30.00	12.00				
Totals				150.00	60.00				

Part 2

GENERAL JOURNAL

Date	Account Titles and Explanation	PR	Debit	Credit

Part 1

GENERAL JOURNAL

Date	Account Titles and Explanation	PR	Debit	Credit

Part 2

GENERAL JOURNAL

Date	Account Titles and Explanation	PR	Debit	Credit

Problem 11-3B

Part 1

GENERAL JOURNAL

Date	Account Titles and Explanation	PR	Debit	Credit

Part 2

GENERAL JOURNAL

Date		Account Titles and Explanation	PR	Debit	Credit

Part 3

GENERAL JOURNAL

Date		Account Titles and Explanation	PR	Debit	Credit

Problem 11-4B

GENERAL JOURNAL

Date		Account Titles and Explanation	PR	Debit	Credit

GENERAL JOURNAL

Date	Account Titles and Explanation	PR	Debit	Credit